The Strategy of Life

Clifford Grobstein

UNIVERSITY OF CALIFORNIA, SAN DIEGO

The
Strategy
of
Life

W. H. Freeman and Company

SAN FRANCISCO AND LONDON

Preface

What is it like to stand at the threshold of an epoch? Those of us alive today should know. Man has moved into space, will shortly land on the moon, and perhaps next on Mars. With these events a long progression—one that has lasted several *billion* years—will reach a climax. Earthly life will escape its confinement and begin its invasion of other parts of the solar system. Whether an event like this has ever occurred before, anywhere in the vastness of the universe, we do not know. If not, we are about to witness not only an enormous step in the history of earthly life, but the opening of a new chapter in the book of the cosmos.

How did this all come about? Was it chance or was it inevitable? Was there a plan and, if so, whose? Is there a strategy that life has followed during its long incubation on earth? This little book contains partial answers to these questions. It is called *The Strategy of Life* because the story it tells is not of a plan or a planner, but of a process—a steady, creative progression of life—upon which hindsight confers the appearance of strategy. The story of life—its premonitions in the stars, its beginnings in the interactions of sun and planet, its fruition during earth's maturation—now seems like an arrow pointed toward man's new adventure. There is something to learn from adopting hindsight's view, from thinking of properties and events—which we can *now* see were indispensable to life as we know it—as though they were strategic foresight. In fact, conscious strategy—in the sense of purpose and design—came very late on the scene, with the arrival of man. Thus, the "strategy" of the title is not conscious or purposeful; it is the resultant of a set of fundamental characteristics—for example, heredity—which life very early found enormously successful, which today underlie all the complexity and variety of the living world, and which have become the central organizing principles of modern biology.

The traditional way to learn biology has been to turn directly to living organisms and study each for itself, allowing appreciation of the wholeness of life to emerge gradually. This procedure recapitulates the history of the science of biology, which began with the study of man and extended to other organisms common in his experience. It took considerable time—and daring—to recognize that human life shares properties common to all life. Only recently have we been able to make confident, general statements about all living things— about life, in toto. Opportunity is thus provided for a new approach to teaching and learning—the possibility of proceeding from the general to the specific, from the forest to the trees.

This is another sense in which it seems appropriate to speak of the "strategy" of life. *Strategy* implies the overall view, in contrast to *tactics*, which deal with the particular and the detailed. There is much detail in the tactics of living, in the unique way each organism goes about its business of survival and propagation. Each organism holds a fascinating story and can be approached for its own interest. Each, however, is a sample—a tactical instance—of a broader strategy, and the instance is more meaningful when the general principle is understood. Even man can be seen as a sample—albeit an atypical one, with many special characteristics—of life's strategy. The effort here, however, is not to characterize particular organisms but the complex of life as a whole. In the second half of the twentieth century, biology for the first time is able to attempt this.

This book is, of course, no treatise, nor is it even a complete and balanced summary of all that biologists know. It is intended simply as a brief introduction in broad, "big picture" strokes, which more detailed study should fill in. As such, it may be read profitably at the beginning of a college course in biology and again (perhaps even more profitably) at its end. It may also prove useful to read without relation to a course, as a condensed statement of biology's overall view of its province, at a time when both biology and life are on the verge of crossing new thresholds.

Biology deals with the nature and activities of living organisms. Like science in general, biology is rooted in the substantial and the material; it assumes that life is knowable as external reality. In probing external reality, biology has important allies in the physical sciences and in the social sciences. Indeed, biology should be thought of as a *sector* of science rather than as an isolated discipline. Along with the rest of science, biology asserts the ultimate comprehensibility of all natural phenomena; it puts its faith in causal analysis, and it relies on the cumulative power of objective and quantitative methods. It is an integral part of science's concerted drive to make sense of the universe—to put all of the phenomena of the universe, including life, into one logical package. Biology's peculiar hallmark, in relation to the rest of science, is its focus on the living.

There is much talk these days of a "revolution" in biology, of a "new biology" totally different from the old. Certainly there has been an enormous quickening in the rate of biological advance, with new and powerful insights whose implications are very broad, both for biology and the human outlook. But is there a new knowledge of life that renders all of the old knowledge obsolete? Is there a new approach to biology that supersedes all others, providing a short cut to the secret of life?

Sometimes it is asserted that the application of physics and chemistry to biological problems has revolutionized biology. There can be no doubt that the electron microscope, the ultracentrifuge, the digital computer, and the scintillation counter have had profound impact. We should recall, however, that Galvani, in 1786, laid the groundwork for the physics of electricity when he observed twitching of the severed legs of a frog in contact with dissimilar metals. The development of the battery and our understanding of the nerve impulse have a common history in this observation; physics and physiology were simultaneously enriched by Galvani. Furthermore, it was physical optics that gave biology the microscope, and geology's Lyell who provided conceptual background for biology's Darwin. Interaction and mutual stimulation between biology and the physical sciences is no new phenomenon of the mid-twentieth century, no revolutionary innovation that can explain the "new biology."

It is also asserted that the introduction of generalization and theory is new and has given revolutionary impetus to biology—that the biology of the past was only a dry catalog of facts, without order or synthesis. But the concept of evolution was one of the great intellectual syntheses of the nineteenth century. So, also, was the concept of the cell, which unified vast bodies of information and which underlies the successes of genetics and physiology in the first half of this century. The fact is that theory and concept are not new to biology; the coupling of fact-gathering with generalization is as old as the science of life itself.

What truly is new is neither technique nor concept, nor any single characteristic. Biology has a new tone because the conscious search for statements of ever broader applicability is succeeding, and these statements are unifying wider and wider areas of the science. One hardly hoped, years ago, that the heredity of bacteria could be discussed in the same terms as—and even illuminate—the heredity of man. No one would have believed that there would be common energetic characteristics in a rose petal and an elephant's ear. At the turn of the century the keynote of biology seemed to be variation and bewildering diversity, but at mid-century we discern underlying similarities everywhere in the living world. There is ground not only to hope, but even to expect, that the complexities of life can be expressed in a manageable number of statements, and that predictions about life may be made from these by deduction. This is to say that, at long last, biology is becoming a full-fledged, logical science.

I say "becoming" to emphasize that what we are discussing still goes on. Biology is burgeoning and is in ferment. If there is a revolution, it is in progress. If there is a new biology, we are still making it. No one can, at this moment, predict with any certainty what biology will be like twenty years hence. The trend of the last decade, however, suggests that the biology of the future will be the product of an increasing multiplicity of approaches, and, paradoxically, that these will converge to yield a unified concept of the nature of life. From studies diversely aimed at molecules, cells, organisms, and populations will come a global conception of earth's biotic film, and from this a projection of this concept to the universe at large. Confidence that we shall achieve this conception also characterizes today's biology. Excitement, confidence, and expectation are in the air, as though all that we now know and say of life is but a prologue. What follows in this book should be seen that way by today's students, for it will be up to them to carry on the play.

May 1965   CLIFFORD GROBSTEIN

Contents

Defining
Life

1

*Life—macromolecular, hierarchically
organized, and characterized by
replication, metabolic turnover, and
exquisite regulation of energy flow—
constitutes a spreading center of order
in a less ordered universe.*

What is life? This question is as old as man's philosophical and
speculative bent, and it is the central question of biology today.
Perhaps it is a measure of our scientific sophistication that we now
know better than to attempt a definitive answer to this question as a
beginning to the study of biology, and that we even wonder sometimes whether it is answerable at all. Yet there is something to be
gained by considering it at the outset.

In one sense we *must* provide an answer. We at least have to say
what we are talking about, what objects or phenomena are denoted
by the term "life" (or "living" or "alive") and are therefore the
business of biology. A first approximation to the answer is not hard
to find. The term "life" refers to men, trees, bees, grass, and similar
objects. Without being able to define the term precisely, we find it
convenient to apply to what we accept as "alive", and to living
things generally.

Once typical members of the class have been designated, we
recognize many other objects that clearly belong to the category of
the living, and still others that equally clearly do not. Biology began
with the study of objects that were obviously living. As experience

widened, however, certain objects gave trouble because they were not so obviously either living or nonliving. It became necessary to ask what it is about the typical examples that led to their placement in the same category: What *is* the set of common properties of bees and grass, for example, that allows us to call them both living? Is the spreading encrustation of a lichen on a damp rock living? Are the rocky fingers of a coral reef living? What is common to bees and lichens, to oaks and sea anemones? What are the common characteristics of the very many kinds of objects we accept as alive? What, *in abstract*, is life?

This question can be answered, but not entirely satisfactorily. The more objects we discover and accept as alive, the fewer and the more attenuated are the common properties we can enumerate for the class, and the more we lose of the rich detail of life as a whole. On reflection, the difficulties seem to be posed by the form of the question itself, which stems from an approach that is outmoded and now perhaps unfruitful.

The search for common properties in all living objects is founded in a view which we now see to be earthbound. Until very recently, biology had little reason to look beyond the earth, except in sheerest speculation. Faced with the mystery of life's origin, biologists have occasionally flirted with the idea of an extraterrestrial source of life, and hence with the possibility of life elsewhere in the universe. Fundamentally, however, biology has confined itself to the earth and has dealt with objects encountered on its surface. To define life has meant to distinguish living objects from other objects on our planet, to draw a line between the living and the nonliving. This led to the search for properties possessed individually or collectively by all living objects, and by none of the nonliving objects, found on the earth.

In recent years another perspective has been emerging. It stems partly from biology's own progress, partly from the altered cosmogony provided by astronomy, and partly from the new awareness, derived from space technology, that man and life are not forever earthbound, but are creatures of the universe. This universal perspective has forced us to seek a new basis for the definition of life— for life can no longer be viewed as merely the least common denominator of objects on earth, but must be seen as a totality in the context of the universe and its evolution.

To appreciate this perspective, let's imagine an Extraterrestrial

Intelligence of about our own intellectual power but possessed of instruments of somewhat greater sensitivity and resolution than our own. Assume that this Intelligence has been scanning and observing the behavior of the universe for millenia. It is aware that our sun is a star of ordinary characteristics for its size and age, and that the sun has a planetary system that is conventional in terms of the laws of celestial mechanics. The chemical compositions of the sun, the planets, and the several satellites of the planets have proved, on cursory inspection, to differ little from those of comparable bodies elsewhere in the known universe. In general, the sun is an undistinguished star in a quite ordinary galaxy in a small and not very intriguing part of the universe.

One day, however, an unprecedented event is observed. A tiny particle is emitted from the planet earth. In the next several days, the particle travels along a perfect trajectory to impact on the earth's single satellite, the moon. Attracted by this event, the Intelligence brings additional instrumentation to bear. Soon other particles are observed to be emitted at irregular intervals from earth. The particles are all of approximately the same mass, some moving into orbits around the earth and others moving off toward other planets or into orbits around the sun. Analysis of the frequency of particle emission and of the paths and character of the particles affords no clue to the source of energy or the conditions determining the pattern of particle emission. The earth apparently possesses unsuspected properties that set it off from most other bodies in the universe and cause it to behave in ways not readily explained.

When still more discriminating instrumentation is focused on this planet, it is revealed to be astonishingly unconventional in several respects. Its temperatures, particularly at its surface, are unusually moderate. Its atmosphere is not only especially rich in oxygen and carbon dioxide but contains a large amount of moisture, in keeping with the fact that much of the planet's surface is covered by water, condensed in large basins. Particularly astounding, however, is the detection at or near the earth's surface of *large amounts of matter in an unusually highly aggregated state*. Atoms appear to have condensed not only into unusual molecules but into molecular aggregates so big that they may be appropriately described as *macromolecules*. These are localized almost exclusively at or near the planetary surface in a kind of film. Highly improbable on thermodynamic grounds, the film of molecules appears to consist of *only a few general types*, but within each type there is *an almost infinite variety of specific kinds*.

Moreover, molecules of the several general types occur as *characteristic complexes* arranged in sheets, spheres, and other three-dimensional configurations of elaborate and specific structure. Some of the highly ordered structures have remarkable properties in the manner in which they *capture, store, and transmit energy*. One kind, for example, is highly effective in trapping the cosmic energy of the sun in the form of chemical bond energy. The captured energy can be passed *in extremely small and controlled steps* through an enormously varied series of chemical reactions, both within the capturing structures—in the form of chemical packages—and between these and other structures. Some of the energy is subsequently released when the large molecules break down to smaller ones, rupturing chemical bonds in the process. The breakdown of large molecules, however, is balanced by the production of new large molecules and new macromolecular structures, as old energy is retransferred and new energy is trapped and added to the old. Despite this *constant turnover of energy and materials*, there is a net increase in the mass of the complexes at higher levels of structure. Even more remarkable than this is that *continuity of properties* is preserved in the large-molecule complexes, despite the inexorable flux. Most significant of all is that this continuity is preserved by means of *replication of the complexes*, in which there is not only new formation of their elements but division of the complexes as a whole. Owing to occasional *spontaneous changes in properties* of the complexes, and to the propagation of resultant variants, the population has become elaborately heterogeneous. In one form or another—and the forms are multitudinous—these molecular aggregates have occupied virtually the entire surface of the earth, visibly altering its character in the process.

This is not all. In diversifying and occupying their earthly environment, the simplest macromolecular complexes have become involved in higher level ones, and these in turn in still higher ones, until an entire *hierarchy of order* has come into existence. Aggregates of each level—based on the replication of the levels below—are able to give rise to more of their own kind. The steady thrust of the more highly ordered has come progressively to dominate the less highly ordered aggregates and is even reordering and transforming the conventional materials of the planet. In this there is for the first time a glimmering of explanation of the anomalous emission of particles that attracted the attention of the Intelligence to the planet earth. Something very like Design or Purpose seems to govern masses of materials that are composed of both macromolecular and conventional stuff, and in these masses even the conventional materials show behaviors not usually associated with bodies having the low kinetic levels of earth. It appears, for example, that an extremely localized and delicately controlled flow of energy is being utilized to control release of other energies so massive as otherwise are seen only in the stars. The subtle exchanges of energy underlie, and presumably initiate, much larger emissions of energy of the sort necessary to eject the observed particles. Is this emission of particles an indication that something very like the Intelligence itself is operating, guiding the peculiar aggregated spawn of earth in its outward spread to invade the rest of the universe?

If we adopt the point of view we gave to the Extraterrestrial Intelligence in this little flight of fancy, we so define life as to distinguish it from other phenomena in the universe and thereby avoid the dilemma caused by the adoption of an earthbound view that seeks to find a least common denominator among objects on earth. We can focus not on individual organisms but on the complex fabric of life as a whole. Our own ordinary experience with life on earth does not lead us to think of living things as elements in a macromolecular, hierarchically organized system which is characterized by metabolic turnover, replication, and exquisite regulation of energy flow and which constitutes a spreading center of order in a less ordered universe. Yet this kind of definition comes closer to encompassing what we now know of the entirety of life than one that reduces life to the least common denominator among diverse organisms. The universal perspective puts life in its broadest context, emphasizing the close linkage and interpenetration between life and nonlife and between life and earth—the only place where we know that life exists. Life and earth have long been inseparable; each has deeply marked the other, and we might almost say that one is an aspect of the other. Intimate interplay between living and nonliving has determined not only the character of life but the character of the planet. To a cosmic observer, the feature of earth that would be of chief interest is that it is a bioplanet. We shall adopt the cosmic view and look at life first against the backdrop of the universe and then against that of its only certainly known niche—the earth.

References

BECKNER, M.
>   *The Biological Way of Thought*. New York, Columbia University Press, 1959.

BONNER, J. T.
>   *The Ideas of Biology*. New York, Harper & Row, 1962.

Life
in
the
2 Universe

*In materials and energy, life stems
from the stars, and the flux of life is at
one with the ceaseless flux of the universe.*

The dominant fact revealed by modern research into the nature of the universe is its overwhelming immensity in time and space. How does life measure up in this vastness? Consider the chart of increasing magnitudes (Figure 2-1). Begin with a mouse as an object of the first order of magnitude. To represent man in the same space, we would have to reduce him ten times; the size of man may be thought of as second order of magnitude. A house would not fit into the space unless we reduced it by another ten times; we may call it an object of the third order of magnitude. An office building could be portrayed in the space only if it were reduced by another ten times; it belongs to the fourth order of magnitude. Orders of magnitude constitute a series of the powers of ten: 10^0, 10^1, 10^2, 10^3, ..., 10^n. Each dimension of a given order of magnitude is multiplied by ten in the next; the increase of successive increments is exponential.

In these terms, Mount Everest, or a city and its environs (New York City, for example), is an object of the sixth order of magnitude; the United States is an object of the eighth order; and the earth is an

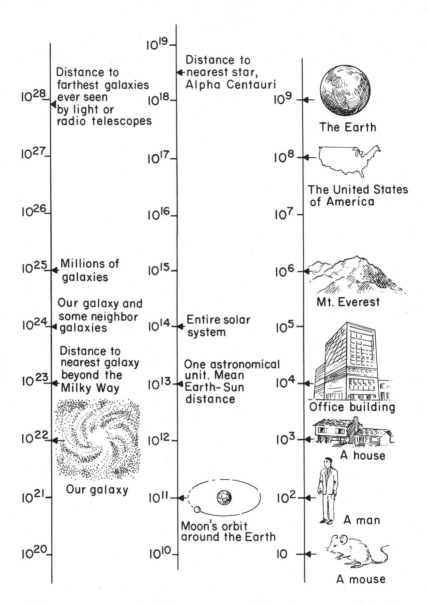

Figure 2-1. *Scale of increasing magnitudes, from 10 cm (size of a mouse) to 10^{28} cm (size of the known universe).*

object of the ninth order. (That is, the diameter of the earth is approximately one million times the length of a mouse.) The moon's orbit around the earth is of 11th order, and the entire solar system, including the orbit of the most distant planet, is of 14th order. Note that from this we move up five orders of magnitude—almost equivalent to going from a mouse to a large city and its environs—before we get to the order of magnitude (the 18th) that includes both the sun and its nearest neighbor-star, α-Centauri. These two stars are four light-years apart. The light-year—the distance traveled by light in one year at a speed of 186,000 miles per second—becomes a convenient unit of distance at the 18th order of magnitude. Before we are able to span our galaxy, in which our sun is but one of about 10^{11} stars, our scale must be increased by four more orders of magnitude (comparable to going from the size of a mouse to the size of a small town). Before we can encompass our galaxy and some of its immediate neighbor-galaxies, our scale must be increased from the 22nd order to the 24th. At this order of magnitude the mega light-year (one million light-years) becomes a convenient unit of distance. When we move up another order of magnitude our home galaxy becomes lost in what appears to be a homogeneous distribution of literally millions of galaxies extending as far as we can "see." Our current limits of astronomical observation are up three additional orders of magnitude, at the 28th, determined so far as we know by the resolution of our devices rather than by an outer limit of the universe. Earthly life, a phenomenon ranging over six or seven orders of magnitude in the vicinity of that of a mouse, is a speck on a speck—and this many times repeated—in the colossal immensity of the universe.

Even more impressive than distance in testifying to the miniscule representation of life in the universe is mass. A fair-sized man may weigh 70 kilograms (7×10^4 grams). A man's weight, in these terms, is of the fourth order of magnitude and the sun's is of the 33rd order. On this scale, our galaxy is believed to weigh in the 44th order of magnitude. Clearly, there is no point in multiplying examples of this immensity. Man dimly sensed immensity when he peered at the distant horizon and attempted to climb hills and mountains in an effort to get closer to the twinkling stars. Later, primitive cosmogony visualized life at the very center of a huge, vaulted sphere. Modern cosmogony removes life from the center of the stage; in fact, it hardly discerns life at all, except on one or more tiny specks—so tiny as not to be thought significant, save by man himself.

Earthly life is but a speck in space, and the life-span of any form of life is the barest instant in time on the clock of the universe. Suppose we establish a year—the time of earth's rotation around the sun—as zero magnitude. Then the life of a cat is of the first order of magnitude; the life of a man, second order. European civilization since the Reformation is of third order, and recorded human history of fourth order. The entire duration of man as a recognizable species is of sixth order. The span of time since the age of dinosaurs is of eighth order; since the first fossils, ninth order ($1-2 \times 10^9$). How long before that life had its origins we can only conjecture, but the best estimates of the age of the earth lie around 4×10^9 years. The age of the solar system is estimated to be only slightly (on a cosmic scale) greater: 5×10^9 years. The galaxy itself may be in the vicinity of 1.5×10^{10} years old, and if there was a "Creation"—in which all we know first appeared—the guess is that this, too, took place about 10^{10} years ago. If man had lived at that time, there could have been 5×10^8 generations since. In contrast, there have been only about one hundred generations (10^2) since the date taken as the beginning of the Christian Era. Life is ancient, man is young, civilization is barely born. An individual life is very short indeed.

The story of life in the universe cannot be fully told without reference to the life history of stars. "Life history" is a biological concept, but recently it has become part of the lexicon of the astronomer. Modern radioastronomy, astrophysics, and astrochemistry increasingly concern themselves with cosmic *processes* instead of seemingly immutable celestial objects. These processes include not only energy transfers and transformations, but the progressive developmental, or evolutionary, changes in the universe as well. Celestial objects are now conceived to begin, mature, age, and end. Metaphorically, they have a life history—individually and perhaps collectively. Involved in their history is the origin and flux of matter itself.

Matter exists in the universe as diffuse gas, as particulate dust, as rocky bodies of various sizes, and as stars. Stars in turn exist in clusters and in larger star-collectives, or galaxies (Figure 2-2). The star is central to all understanding of the organization of matter in

Figure 2-2. *The Great Nebula in Andromeda—a vast star-collective with two smaller satellite clusters, seen against a background of individual stars. [Copyright © Mount Wilson and Palomar Observatories.]*

the universe, for it now appears that stars are cauldrons within which massive conversions of matter and energy occur. Through these cauldrons most, if not all, of the matter of the universe has passed; within them is the birthplace of the elements, from tiny hydrogen to atomically massive uranium.

Stars are not all alike. The bright twinkling objects in the night sky which are commonly called stars include the planets and even a few of the nearer and brighter galaxies. These are, of course, quite different from stars. Even among the true stars, however, there is great variation in size, color, luminosity, mass, and distance from earth. Cataloguing the tens of millions of stars in our own galaxy, let alone those of the tens of millions of other galaxies, is an enormous task. The number of stars is actually inconceivable. As we look out into the universe, we see countless stars in every direction. Moreover, there is no reason at the moment to believe that things would look very different if our vantage point were located elsewhere in the universe. Except that neighboring stars and galaxies would be in different patterns, there would be stars in galactic array as far as we could see. So far as we are now entitled to guess from the evidence, the universe may be limitless and the number of stars infinite.

The variety of stars, however, is not infinite. There are relatively few *kinds* of stars, and these fall into a meaningful pattern. The pattern makes sense if we assume that stars change with time; that they have certain properties when they originate; that these properties alter over long periods of time; and that stars come to an end, scattering their matter and energy back into the universe at large (Figure 2-3). During these processes, it is now believed, all the matter and energy that ever enter into living things were created, and eligible niches for life were provided. Clearly we must understand something of this if we are to understand the background of life.

The history of a star's life can, of course, only be inferred. A sequence of events is postulated by assuming that observable kinds of stars represent stages in a continuous process of change in individual stars. No one has ever seen the entire sequence or even a large part of it; probably no one ever will. Yet the story put together by modern astronomy and nuclear physics hangs together well and inspires our confidence. To tell it, we must recall that neutrons and protons are the chief constituents of atomic nuclei. Neutrons and protons are of approximately equal mass, but differ in that protons have positive charge and neutrons have no charge. Neutrons and protons are attracted and held in association by extremely short-range, but incredibly powerful, nuclear fields. Protons are repelled from each other by their like charge, as are electrons outside the nucleus. Within the atomic nucleus an equilibrium exists between nuclear attraction exerted among protons and neutrons, and electric repulsion exerted

Figure 2-3. *The Crab Nebula. This is not a star-collective, but is believed to be a gas cloud produced by a stellar explosion observed in* A.D. *1054. Most of the mass of the star is returning to diffuse interstellar matter.* [*Copyright © Mount Wilson and Palomar Observatories.*]

among the protons. Beyond the nucleus are the orbits of whirling electrons, on whose behavior atomic interaction depends (Figure 2–4). The distribution of electrons in any atom is the resultant of electron-proton *attraction* and electron-electron *repulsion*—electrical forces which are balanced in the stable configurations of electrons characteristic of each atomic species.

It turns out that there is a close connection between the nature of atoms and the classification of stars. Among the stars of any general neighborhood, one finds an important relationship between the in-

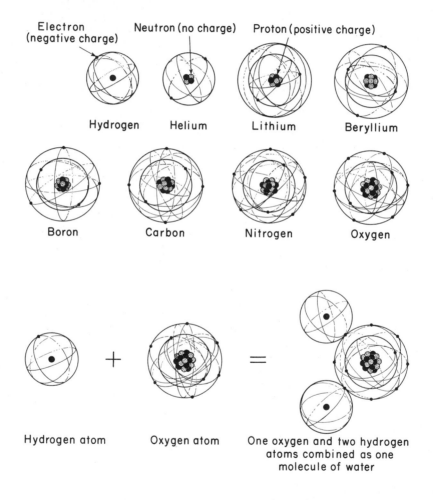

Figure 2-4. *Neutrons, protons, and electrons in the configurations of atoms.*

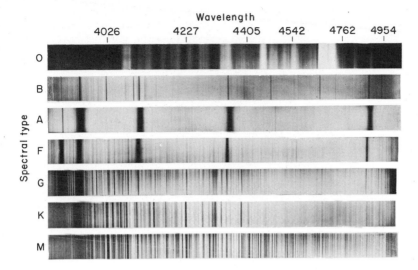

Figure 2-5. *Characteristic wavelength patterns, or light spectra, from various star types (labeled at left). Note different band patterns for each star type. [Copyright © University of Michigan Observatory.]*

tensity of their light emission, or intrinsic brightness, and their surface temperature. Surface temperature in turn is related to the character of the light emitted, particulary to the wavelength pattern, or spectrum, of the light reaching us from the star (Figure 2-5). We interpret the spectrum in terms of the atomic composition of the star. When brightness and spectral type are plotted against each other for a sample series of stars close to the sun, a regular relationship appears. This is shown in the Hertzsprung-Russell diagram (Figure 2-6), named after the discoverers of the relationship. The diagram shows that, except for significant deviations that we will come to in a moment, the stars cluster along a "main sequence," which runs from the lower right to the upper left of the diagram. This means that in the population of stars sampled, there is a large fraction in which spectrum type, and hence atomic composition, is closely related to brightness. Notice that from right to left on the diagram, spectrum type in this main sequence shifts with increasing brightness from the red toward the blue. Now what does this mean?

For several centuries it has been assumed that stars form by con-

THE STRATEGY OF LIFE

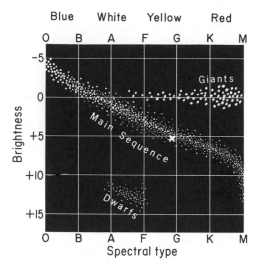

Figure 2-6. *Relationship between brightness and spectral type in a sample of stars. Most fall into a broad zone called the main sequence.* [*From Christiansen and Garrett,* Structure and Change: An Introduction to the Science of Matter, *1960,* W. H. Freeman and Co., *San Francisco.*]

densation of the diffuse, gaseous, interstellar medium. There is reason to belive that this process continues even now under favorable circumstances within galaxies (Figure 2-7). Condensation means aggregation of matter, in this instance presumably through gravitational attraction. In the process of falling toward each other in condensation, particles increase in kinetic energy, and the matter that they compose heats up. Condensation of the enormous quantities of matter involved in a star means that temperatures are elevated into the range of millions and tens of millions of degrees. As temperatures increase through this range the particles are accelerated to such high velocities that, upon collision, fusion reactions can occur between them (Figure 2-8); that is, protons are moving fast enough to overcome electrical repulsion and to come within range of the powerful attractive nuclear forces. In the simplest such reaction, two protons (hydrogen nuclei, H^1) become coupled; one converts to a neutron by emission of a positron, and a deuteron (heavy hydrogen) nucleus D^2 is formed. As deuterons are formed in quantity, the probability increases that they too will collide and fuse to form helium nuclei. Three helium nuclei may in turn fuse to form a carbon nucleus, and so on. It is important to note that as aggregation goes on and nuclear size increases, it takes greater and greater kinetic energy to add additional particles; that is, higher and higher temperatures are required. To build helium, 10×10^6 degrees is required; for carbon, oxygen, and neon, 100×10^6 degrees; for magnesium, silicon, sulfur, and calcium, 1000×10^6 degrees; and for iron, 3000×10^6 degrees.

Figure 2-7. *Luminous cloud in the constellation of Scutum Sobieski. The brightness is due to the presence of many hot young stars. The dark patches may be places where new stars are forming.* [*Copyright © Mount Wilson and Palomar Observatories.*]

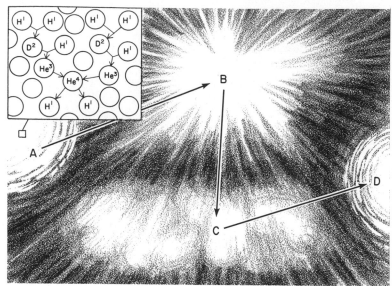

Figure 2-8. *Cycle of matter in stars. As shown in inset at upper left, hydrogen (H¹)*
fusion in star A forms deuterium (D²) and helium (He³, He⁴). Much
later, star A may explode, as at B, to yield interstellar dust (C). D is
a second-generation star produced by sweeping up of interstellar dust
partly derived from A.

Thus the concentration of primordial matter produces not only an
increase in the probability of particle collision, but an increase in
temperature, and hence an increase in energy of interaction. The
first interaction to be expected is the condensation of hydrogen to
form helium; that is, condensation of primordial matter consisting
mainly of protons will lead to hydrogen fusion. In terminology that
has become all too familiar in another context, the condensing star
sets off a thermonuclear fusion reaction, forming helium from hydrogen and liberating enormous quantities of energy. As we shall see,
it is this kind of energy, liberated in the sun, upon which all of earthly
life depends.

"Young" stars—those still in the process of condensation—may be
expected to be relatively cool, of low luminosity, and to occur to the
right of the main sequence on the Hertzsprung-Russell diagram. As
they condense and heat up due to contraction, they move toward
the main sequence and eventually become part of it. Indeed, all of

the stars of the main sequence turn out to be stars within which hydrogen fusion occurs and is the primary source of their energy emission. Stars remain in equilibrium in the main sequence, generating energy by hydrogen fusion and radiating an equal amount into space until their hydrogen is exhausted. The duration of equilibrium varies inversely with the mass of the star. Large young stars become very hot, move into the upper part of the main sequence, produce and radiate energy very rapidly, and persist there for only a short time. For example, stars twenty times the mass of the sun are estimated to exhaust their hydrogen in only 10 million years. Stars of about the same mass as the sun may persist in the middle region of the main sequence for more than 10 billion years, and stars one-fifth the mass of the sun may be expected to remain in the lower region of the main sequence for 100 times as long.

The abundance of stars of the main sequence (perhaps 80–85% of all stars) suggests that hydrogen fusion occupies a large fraction of the life span of a star. The sun, for example, is powered by hydrogen fusion and does not appear to have changed materially in its energy emission and temperature in the 4.5 billion year history of the solar system. The sun goes on "burning" 564 million tons of hydrogen into helium every second, liberating in each second as much energy as would the explosion of several million H-bombs. Yet it has sufficient mass to last many billions of years longer. The life of stars does, however, have a limit. As a star ages, the gradual depletion of hydrogen and the accumulation of helium change it in important ways. In particular, the heavier helium product gravitates toward the center of the star, undergoes contraction, and grows still hotter. Whereas central temperatures of main-sequence stars remain stable during the period of hydrogen fusion, the central temperatures of older stars become favorable for helium fusion and the formation of heavier elements.

We cannot trace here in detail the interesting facts and speculation concerning subsequent stellar senescence. Suffice it to say that such relatively infrequent phenomena as pulsating stars, red giants, novae, and white dwarfs are assumed to represent steps along the path toward stellar death. When stars die, vast quantities of matter are returned to interstellar space, sometimes in the spectacular explosions of supernovae, perhaps more often by the relatively slow loss of surplus material through outward streaming or a kind of cos-

Indeed, there is indirect evidence that some stars have invisible companions, either smaller stars or planetary satellites. These cannot be seen directly, but the presence of smaller bodies is postulated because there are perturbations in the movement of their larger companions that are difficult to explain in any other way. This is slim evidence on which to postulate life outside our solar system; the postulate is bolstered by the suggestion that failure to accept it constitutes narrow provincialism. After all, some argue, man first thought of himself as being at the center of things—first of a flat earth, then of the firmament of stars. Frustrated in this, he fell back to the idea of an orbit around a key central star. Now we know that the star is not even at the center of its own galaxy. We know also that the galaxy itself is but one of a myriad of galaxies that recede each from the others in all directions. The universe has no center, least of all where we are; our star is one of billions. Why then assume that life exists only here, the argument runs; why indulge human conceit any longer? Surely the probability is high that among millions of stars with planets there are others like ours; surely life is no isolated miracle, but the general and inevitable consequence of stellar and material evolution.

This is the argument of those who are exponents of life as an essential and widespread manifestation of universal evolution. It is an exciting conception, this modern version of genesis—truly a synthesis of man, life, and the universe. There are skeptics, however, and their arguments also are persuasive, if not nearly so alluring. They note that there is not a shred of really conclusive direct evidence for life anywhere but on the earth. They point out that the panbiotic argument is reasonable speculation but is logically specious. The frequency of known bioplanets at the moment is one (one bioplanet in one sample), and the frequency of known solar systems containing a bioplanet is one. Therefore, no statement of probability can be made, no matter how many solar systems and planets may exist. Until we know that our limited sample does *not* contain the only bioplanet, we can make no valid predictions about the probability of finding another. We must wait for data establishing the existence of extraterrestrial life in our own solar system, or in at least one other, before the panbiotic hypothesis will acquire credibility.

The issue could be settled in our lifetime; it may await the ingenuity and imagination of many succeeding generations. But until it is settled the issue will increasingly agitate men's minds, for within it is the key to the next step in man's widening perspective, his fuller understanding of life's place—and his own—in the seemingly endless flux of the universe.

References

BURBIDGE, GEOFFREY, AND BURBIDGE, MARGARET
  "Stellar Populations." *Scientific American*, November 1958 (Offprint No. 203, W. H. Freeman and Company, San Francisco).

FOWLER, WILLIAM A.
  "The Origin of the Elements." *Scientific American*, September 1956 (Offprint No. 210, W. H. Freeman and Company, San Francisco).

GREENSTEIN, JESSE L.
  "Dying Stars." *Scientific American*, January 1959 (Offprint No. 216, W. H. Freeman and Company, San Francisco).

HOYLE, FRED
  Astronomy. Garden City, Doubleday, 1962.

OVENDEN, M. W.
  Life in the Universe. Garden City, Doubleday (Anchor Book), 1962.

PAGE, THORNTON
  Stars and Galaxies. Englewood Cliffs, Prentice-Hall, 1962.

SINGH, S.
  Great Ideas and Theories of Modern Cosmology. New York, Dover, 1961.

TOCQUET, R.
  Life on the Planets. New York, Grove Press, 1962.

Life
on
Earth

3

*Life on earth—a highly heterogeneous
thin film at the surface—constantly
responds to earthly changes and constantly
produces changes in the earth; the histories
of the two are inextricably intertwined
in the progression of the bioplanet.*

Although what we seek is a general picture of life in the universe,
life on earth is our unique, present source of direct information. In
this chapter, rather than approach life as observers participating in
the phenomenon, we shall attempt to approach it from without and
characterize it in entirety as one of the major features of the planet.
Such an approach requires special effort to comprehend phenomena
that are above or below our own scale of magnitudes; it is easy to
look at organisms, but it is harder to see and comprehend the matrix
of which they are part. The effort, however, yields a new perspective,
like viewing a city from the top of its tallest building.

Life does not exist everywhere in and on the earth. Rather it is confined to a thin shell that includes particularly the interfaces among
land, air, and water. It is a remarkable fact that, in general, life does
not exist in depth within any one of these earthly phases—not very
far down in the land masses, nor very high in the atmosphere, nor
very abundantly in the abyss of the oceans. Characteristically, life is

abundant at the interfaces between phases. Life's habitat is the relatively thin zone where land, sea, and sky meet. We call this inhabited
region of earth the biosphere.

What sets limits to the biosphere? Life exists in the atmosphere, for
example, but is not abundantly present everywhere in it. Why?
Gravity is the prime reason; a body of any size must expend energy
continuously to keep itself suspended in the atmosphere. Density of
the atmosphere decreases rapidly with altitude, because gravity holds
most of the atmosphere close to the earth. As density decreases, the
expenditure of energy required to keep a body in suspension increases. Only very small objects can remain suspended high in the
atmosphere. At great heights, however, temperatures are unfavorable, bombardment by cosmic radiation increases, and the concentration of essential gases, such as carbon dioxide and oxygen, becomes
extremely low. The upper atmosphere has been penetrated only by
man, because only man has been able to utilize sources of energy
sufficient to transport himself in a vehicle within which he can control the environment.

Life moves down into cracks and crevices in the earth; how far, no
one knows for certain. The major obstacle to its penetration of earth
is the absence of light. The energetic foundation of all life is con-
verted solar energy—the radiated output of thermonuclear fusion in
the core of the sun. Some living organisms can exist indefinitely in
the dark of deep caves, but with few exceptions they do so only by
virtue of transfer to them of energy-rich compounds made by organisms living in the light. Thus, the fringes of life may reach the
dark recesses of the earth, but they must remain close enough to the
main body of life to permit rapid and effective exchange. That this
is true is evident from the distribution of life in the oceans. Here
there are no mechanical barriers, as there are on land. Nor does
temperature rise byond the tolerance of life, as probably occurs with
increasing depth into the earth. Nonetheless, the life-content of the
abyss of the sea is to the life-content near the surface as a desert is to
a jungle. Deserts are relatively sterile due to lack of water; the abyss
is relatively sterile due to lack of light, which is absorbed in the
waters above.

The biosphere, therefore, is the thin shell of land, sea, and sky
within which life receives either direct illumination or, indirectly,
the energy-rich products of photochemical reactions. Life exists vir-

tually everywhere within its boundaries. Is there, in fact, any place on the surface of the earth or in the seas where life does not exist? Not in the heart of a volcano. Probably not in the long-frozen water of the arctic ice pack. Certainly not for some days in the crater of a thermonuclear explosion. But such places are few. In fact, it is hard to imagine a site on the surface of the earth that is totally sterile, entirely without some form of life. Everywhere life presses against the boundaries of unfavorable environments and manages in some way to transcend them.

The relation of temperature to life provides a good example of life's invasive pressure. The temperature spectrum of the earth is undoubtedly the most significant of the features that qualify it as a bioplanet. Temperatures range over millions of degrees throughout the universe, but the tolerance of life is limited to a range of something less than 300°C. Most organisms prefer temperatures between 10° and 40°C., yet the frozen arctic and antarctic have flourishing flora and fauna, and some microorganisms regularly inhabit and reproduce in hot springs at temperatures close to the boiling point of water (85–88°C). Within the confines of the biosphere, "where there is a will there is a way."

Clearly, however, life is not equally distributed everywhere. The term "biomass" is applied to the total quantity of material that makes up the living organisms present in a given area. The biomass of the earth has never been measured. We have no idea how much the entire biota of the earth would weigh at this moment, nor do we know how the figure would change with the seasons or from year to year or from era to era. For local regions, however, the biomass can be determined or estimated. Measurements confirm what ordinary experience suggests—that some parts of the biosphere are more favorable to life than others. The productivity per day of new organic material has been measured in different parts of the biosphere (Figure 3-1). Deserts produce less than 0.5 gram of dry organic matter per square meter per day; grasslands and mountain forests produce 0.5–3.0 grams; moist forests and grasslands produce 3–10 grams (comparable with most agriculture). The productivity of the relatively shallow waters of the continental shelf is comparable to those of grasslands and mountain forests, and the productivity of deep oceans is comparable to that of deserts. Life occurs everywhere in the biosphere, but it occurs in patches of greater and lesser abun-

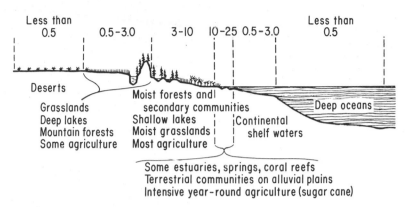

Figure 3-1. *Productivity of different regions of the biosphere, expressed in grams of dry matter per square meter per day.* [*From Odum,* Fundamentals of Ecology, *1959, Saunders, Philadelphia.*]

dance, in conformity with local variation in land forms.

Clearly, then, the biomass is quantitatively heterogeneous. It is, of course, also qualitatively heterogeneous. Measurement of total dry organic mass tells us something of the living state, but it reveals little of the complexity of the processes involved within the functioning biomass. We know that several parameters, such as availability of solar energy, water, and basic raw materials (for example, carbon dioxide, oxygen, and minerals), play an important role in controlling the biomass. We also know, however, that important interactions go on within the biomass itself, particularly between the unlike units that invariably characterize it. A fundamental property of the biomass is its organization into assemblages of different kinds of units—groups of organisms that exist in characteristic associations with each other and with their environment. These associations are not just statistical regularities in the frequency distribution of kinds of organisms; they are functional groupings essential to the behavior of the whole biomass and of its component organisms. To these functional subsystems of the biomass, we apply the term "ecosystem."

We have said that the biomass depends fundamentally upon the utilization of solar energy (Figure 3-2). Not all components of the biomass, however, are able to capture solar energy. Those that do are said to be "photoautotrophic," or self-nourishing in the presence of light. They require, generally speaking, only light and simple in-

Figure 3-2. *Energy cycles of the biosphere are powered by the sun. Land plants bind solar energy into organic compounds (heavy broken arrows) utilized successively by herbivores, carnivores, and scavengers; residual compounds are decomposed by bacteria (light solid arrows). Energy is fixed by microscopic sea plants through a similar "food chain" (heavy solid arrows). In the water cycle (light broken arrows) water evaporated from the sea is precipitated on land and used by living organisms, and eventually returns to the sea bearing minerals and organic matter.* [*From Cole,* Scientific American, *April 1958.*]

organic substances to produce organic materials. In the process they absorb photic energy and transform simple molecules into complex chemical compounds that are essential to their own functioning but which also are enriched in energy that is releasable in subsequent decomposition. The photoautotrophic organisms, mainly green plants, make up one large component of the biomass. A second component includes the "heterotrophic" (more precisely, "phago-trophic") organisms, mainly animals, which feed upon the autotrophs. They cannot utilize raw photic energy themselves, but they are highly effective in obtaining it from the compounds made by the autotrophs. They build up new complex compounds essential to their own functioning, and they release in the process smaller molecules that are important raw materials for the autotrophs. A basic cycle of energy and materials is thus set up within the ecosystem— from sun and earth to autotroph, from autotroph to heterotroph, from heterotroph back to earth, and so on. The steady supply of new energy from the sun powers the cycle and replenishes the inevitable leakage of energy out of the system in the form of nonrecoverable heat.

Only the barest indication of the dynamic nature of the biomass is revealed in this description of the basic cycle of interaction among sun, earth, autotroph, and heterotroph. For example, in addition to the photoautotrophs there are chemoautotrophs, mainly specialized bacteria, which can produce organic materials from inorganic by extracting energy from oxidizable substrates. Among the hetero-trophs alone there is vast variety. Some, the herbivores, feed directly on autotrophs. Others, the carnivores, feed on the herbivores. Carni-vores frequently feed upon one another. Within a given ecosystem an element such as carbon, nitrogen, or phosphorus may move through a number of steps of synthesis and breakdown before completing its cycle from earth back to earth. The cycle passes through character-istic sequences of organisms—food chains—that differ for each eco-system. In each ecosystem there is a characteristic, continuing, and complex flux of energy; each ecosystem has a *metabolism* of its own.

An ecosystem may be very large and complex or relatively small and simple. For certain purposes the entire biomass may be thought of as a single ecosystem, the "ecosphere." This is worth mentioning if only to emphasize that, metabolically, there are no completely isolated parts of the biomass. Although it is useful to isolate smaller

ecosystems or individual organisms conceptually, they are never entirely isolated in reality. For example, the entire biomass interacts
with the atmosphere, whose oxygen and carbon dioxide are "compartments" of the biosphere through which flow occurs to and from
the biomass. The relatively constant oxygen content of the atmosphere (about 20 percent) is an equilibrium value that depends on the
overall constancy of the character of the biomass and on rapid diffu-
sion and effective mixing within the atmosphere. The community,
or "pool," property of the atmosphere with respect to the biomass
has been dramatically illustrated in recent years by the world-wide
concern with radioactive fallout from thermonuclear explosions.
Once injected into the atmosphere by the biomass, radioactive materials of sufficient half-life cannot be excluded from any sector of the
biomass. It may be a long time before we fully understand the complex of interactions that occur within the ecosphere, and probably
still longer before we comprehend its implications for the human
community. What is emphasized here is that all of earthly life, for
certain important purposes, can be conceived to be a single ecosystem.

More complete accounts can be given of interactions within
smaller and simpler ecosystems than for the entire ecosphere. There
is a certain arbitrariness in delineating ecosystems within the larger
ecosphere, but if the arbitrariness is kept in mind, extremely useful
analyses can be made. One can ask questions about the overall behavior of such an ecosystem as a pond, a forest, an island, or a desert.
One may set up artificial or model systems for their general interest
or for their relevance to the problems of such *man-made* ecosystems
as an isolated space capsule. In each system one can investigate the
balance sheet of input and output of energy and material, the nature
of the flow of energy and material through the system, and the effect
of variation of one living component upon others. For example,
Odum has described some of the major parameters of simple terrestrial (grassland) and aquatic (pond) ecosystems (Figure 3-3). Each
has its characteristic nonliving (abiotic) substrate of organic and inorganic substances. Each has an autotrophic component—the vegetation of the terrestrial system and the floating phytoplankton of the
aquatic system. Both ecosystems have primary consumers who feed
directly on the autotrophs, and secondary consumers who feed on
the primary, and so on. The mass and activity of the autotrophic

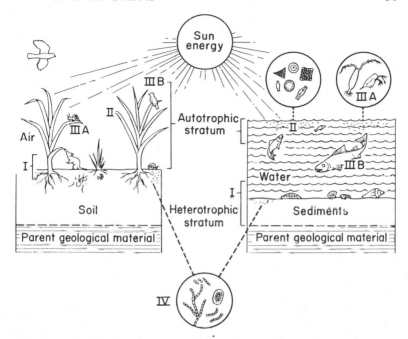

Figure 3-3. *Correspondence of components of terrestrial (left) and aquatic (right) ecosystems. I = abiotic components, II = photoautotrophs, IIIA = primary consumers, IIID = secondary consumers, IV = decomposers. [After Odum,* Ecology, *copyright © 1963 by Holt, Rinehart and Winston, Inc., New York.]*

component can be measured in the pond by determining the chlorophyll content at various depths. (Chlorophyll is the photosensitive pigment in all plant cells that "fixes" solar energy in the visible light range.) Samples of pond water collected at known depths can be analyzed chemically for total chlorophyll content. The values obtained can be interpreted in terms of organic material synthesized and made available for heterotrophic consumption; that is, the autotrophic productivity can be calculated.

Similarly, samples of pond water can be sieved to collect the zooplankton, the small, floating heterotrophs that feed on the phytoplankton. Screening yields the somewhat larger organisms that feed on the zooplankton, and netting captures the still larger fish, crayfish, and other secondary carnivores. By fractioning the biomass of the pond in this way, one can get quantitative data on the size of each component, on the total productivity of the biomass, and on the part of the total photic energy captured by each component of the biomass. In short, one can consider the pond to consist of a series of trophic levels among which the transformations can be traced and measured.

This sort of analysis speedily convinces the ecologist that the qualitative heterogeneity of the biomass—that is, the multiplicity of kinds of living units, or organisms, within it—is by no means random or chaotic, but occurs in a pattern that is important to the functioning of each ecosystem. Significantly, heterogeneity of the biomass occurs not only in terms of broad trophic function (autotroph, heterotroph, and their divisions) but within these major divisions as well. There is not just one kind of autotroph or heterotroph in an ecosystem; there are many kinds, and they are distributed in particular relationships. Moreover, if one analyzes the abundance of particular kinds or species of organisms, striking regularities appear. One of these is that any given category or division of an ecosystem—for example, its primary heterotrophs—contains a few species whose numbers are relatively abundant, but a large number of other species whose members are relatively rare. Thus, the population of any component of an ecosystem tends to be diverse in number of kinds, but emphasizes strongly a few of the kinds. Forests are usually characterized by a dominant member species, such as lodgepole pine, but contain a scattering of many other kinds of trees. Indeed, practical experience has shown that it is very difficult to maintain a pure population of a single kind of organism, whether in the laboratory or in agriculture.

The explanation for particular patterns of diversity of species within ecosystems is not fully elucidated, but it seems clear that it reflects, in part, the diversity of the biosphere. For example, more than one kind of photoautotroph occurs in an ecosystem when light conditions are not the same throughout the system. If one examines the several kinds, one finds that each has a slightly different photosynthetic pigment and that these pigments vary in their sensitivity, depending on the intensity and wavelength of the incident light. For example, pigments that are highly efficient in fixing the dim light deep in a pond are operative but inefficient in fixing the intense light close to the pond's surface. At least two kinds of photic capture are necessary in this ecosystem if there is to be maximum efficiency over the entire range of light intensity. Maximum efficiency might be achieved either by one organism capable of adjusting to the entire intensity range (euryphotic) or by two organisms each capable of existing in the middle range but of adjusting to opposite ends (steno-photic). Either way, the ecosystem as a whole would have higher overall efficiency. The more frequent alternative, one finds, involves two kinds of organisms.

Diversity within the ecosystem, therefore, is in part a reflection of diversity of environment. But why is there not a single kind of organism for each environment? What is the significance of the fact that there are often many relatively rare satellite species clustered around the dominant one? The answer becomes clear only when we watch the ecosystem for a period of time. It is important to note that not only do the properties of the biosphere vary at any given time, but they also vary from time to time. Correspondingly, the biomass is not only heterogeneous in space but in time. In particular, it is capable of adjusting in order to maintain itself in the face of environmental change.

Suppose an ecosystem comprises three water-dwelling photosynthetic organisms. Two (D and B in Figure 3-4) may be of maximum photosynthetic efficiency in dim (D) and bright (B) light, respectively, and each of declining efficiency at intermediate depths. Assume organism B to be maintained at the surface because it has developed some flotation device such as oil droplets, while organism D is less buoyant and is in equilibrium well below the surface. A third organism (C) is of lesser photosynthetic efficiency than either B or D in their most favored depths, but is more efficient than either in the intermediate depths.

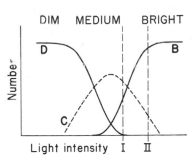

Figure 3-4. *Hypothetical relations among three photosynthetic organisms in an ecosystem.*

Moreover, C is capable of living either at the surface or in deeper water. At a light intensity of II, C will be a relatively rare associate of the dominant organisms, D and B, at their favored depths, since each is far more efficient at the light intensities prevalent there. Suppose, however, that the light intensity is drastically reduced to I—perhaps by overgrowth of a pond by lily pads. Then C will be more efficient than B at the new light intensity, and hence will become the dominant species at the surface. Meanwhile, D will be much reduced in number or eliminated, because virtually no light gets through to the lower depths and D cannot ascend to the upper level, where light intensity would be favorable for it.

Thus, the significance of low numbers of C in the ecosystem when light intensity is high does not become obvious until the light intensity is drastically reduced. Then it is seen that in the presence of C the total productivity of the pond is less altered by environmental change than it would be in C's absence. By themselves B and D would fail to maintain autotrophic productivy of the pond at low light intensity. The differential efficiency of C maintains productivity despite the change in lighting.

If the argument can be generalized, it indicates that the diversity of the biomass increases the range of occupancy of the environment by living systems, and also the stability of such systems in the face of environmental change. The response of an ecosystem to environmental change is seen most spectacularly in the events following massive destruction of biomass in a particular area—by a forest fire, for example. The repopulation of such an area takes place in a regular series of steps referred to as *succession*. The important point to recognize at the moment is that each stage in succession involves different kinds of organisms, each appropriate to the state of the local biosphere at that time (Figure 3-5). A denuded and sterile area must acquire a population of autotrophs before it can support heterotrophs. The first heterotrophs must be primary consumers, and their activities, together with those of the autotrophs, must so alter conditions as to allow secondary heterotrophs to move in. The kinds of plants and animals change continuously during succession in keeping with the alteration and restoration of physical and chemical conditions. Kinds of organisms abundant at the beginning of the succession may be rare or absent at the end, and the compositional changes of the biomass are part of the continuity and effectiveness of the ecosystem as a whole. The regularity of these successional events makes it clear that regulatory systems exist within the biomass, and between biomass and biosphere, which keep changes in

Time in years	1 – 10	10 – 25	25 – 100	100+
Community type	Grassland	Shrubs	Pine forest	Hardwood forest

Grasshopper sparrow
Meadowlark
Field sparrow
Yellowthroat
Yellow-breasted chat
Cardinal
Towhee
Bachman's sparrow
Prairie warbler
White-eyed vireo
Pine warbler
Summer tanager
Carolina wren
Carolina chickadee
Blue-gray gnatcatcher
Brown-headed nuthatch
Wood pewee
Hummingbird
Tufted titmouse
Yellow-throated vireo
Hooded warbler
Red-eyed vireo
Hairy woodpecker
Downy woodpecker
Crested flycatcher
Wood thrush
Yellow-billed cuckoo
Black and white warbler
Kentucky warbler
Acadian flycatcher

	Grassland	Shrubs	Pine forest	Hardwood forest
Number of common species*	2	8	15	19
Density (pairs per 100 acres)	27	123	113	233

*A common species is arbitrarily designated as one with a density of 5 pairs per 100 acres or greater in one or more of the 4 community types.

Figure 3-5. *The general pattern of secondary succession on abandoned farmland in the southeastern United States. The upper diagram shows four stages in the life form of the vegetation (grassland, shrubs, pines, hardwoods); the bar graph shows changes in passerine bird population that accompany the changes in autotrophs. A similar pattern will be found in any area where a forest is climax, but the species of plants and animals that take part in the development series will vary according to the climate or topography of the area. [From Odum,* Ecology, *© 1963 by Holt, Rinehart and Winston, Inc., New York.]*

one or the other in close correlation. Heterogeneity of kind within the biomass plays an important role in adjustive change.

The biomass responds to environmental change on the long-term scale of evolution as well as on the relatively short-term scale of succession. At any given moment, the biomass may contain many kinds of organisms, and it may adjust to environmental change by altering the proportions of these kinds. In the short run, this is all that can be done. The pond choked with lily pads can change the composition of its species relatively quickly, increasing the number of those whose chlorophyll is more efficient in dim light. In the long run, however, there is another possibility. If the environmental change is slower (for example, if light intensity is gradually reduced due to increasing dust in the atmosphere over a period of a century), then the chlorophyll of species B may be so modified as to be more efficient at lower light intensity, or species D may so alter as to float higher in the water. Thus, the composition of species within the ecosystem might remain unaltered, but one or more species would change in properties, thereby maintaining the effectiveness of the biomass through evolutionary change in species. The capacity of species to alter their properties in a continuous, stable, long-term progression was obviously important to the appearance of diversity on the scene in the first place, and this capacity to evolve continues to play an essential role in the interactions between biomass and biosphere.

In summary, life on earth is a thin film that exists primarily at the surface and is highly heterogeneous, both quantitatively and qualitatively. It is a patterned fabric in that it consists of multitudinous units and collectives united by a complex of interactions. Matter and energy flow through the film in complex courses, and the film itself is constantly altering in properties in response to environmental change. The continuing interplay between life and earth have so closely interwoven the two that the history and properties of one can scarcely be discussed without reference to the other. The progressive changes of life and earth are inextricably intertwined in the story of the earth as a bioplanet—the only such planet currently known.

References

COKER, R. F.
  This Great and Wide Sea. New York, Harper & Row (Torchbook 551), 1962.

DOWDESWELL, W. H.
  General Ecology. New York, Harper & Row (Torchbook 543), 1962.

ODUM, E. P.
  Ecology. New York, Holt, Rinehart & Winston, 1963.

Levels
of
4 Organization

*Life is characterized by a hierarchy
of structure and of functional control
that spans the range from the
minuteness of atomic and molecular
interactions to the relatively
enormous communication distances
achieved by human society in ordering itself.*

In attempting to characterize the entire biomass, we have been forced to recognize that it has components and that statements about the properties of the whole biomass or its components cannot be fully separated from each other. We have seen that the entire biota of the earth makes up an ecosystem, which for certain purposes must be viewed as an integrated whole, but for other purposes must be recognized to have smaller subsystems within it, such as ponds, fields, and forests. Within these, too, there are functional compartments— autotrophs, heterotrophs, and their subdivisions, which are the individual living organisms of ordinary experience. We can generalize all of this by saying that the biomass is organized in successively encompassing levels of interacting components or units. Any biological phenomenon we choose to analyze lies within, or is a product of, this hierarchy of interacting units.

In this chapter we shall concentrate on this hierarchical aspect of the biomass, its organization in components of successively lower order. We can begin with almost any component, because the fundamental units and levels of order throughout the biomass are generally similar. We have already referred to two fundamental levels—the ecosystem and the organism. These are not always simply and sharply delineated; distinguishable ecosystems may interact as parts of a larger ecosystem, and it is frequently useful to recognize certain *groups* of organisms as intermediate components of an ecosystem. We designate ecosystem and organism as major levels, and the others as subdivisions, partly because of what we know of the nature of the biomass and partly because of convenience and habit. These designations will be used in what follows.

Organisms are interacting units within ecosystems, but they in turn are frequently composed of interacting cells (Figure 4-1). Again, we have some troubles in definition, for there are organisms that do not have component cells (unicellular or acellular, such as amoeba), and there are others in which cells occur in collectives (tissues and organs) that are regarded for certain purposes as intermediate components of organisms. Cells as components, however, are so ubiquitous, and their properties as units so fundamental to the behavior of organisms

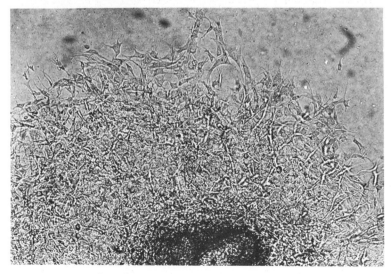

Figure 4-1. *A bit of mouse tissue in a culture dish, with individual cells migrating out of the mass.*

and ecosystems, that the cell is generally accepted as a third major
level of biological organization.

Though cells are units in certain situations and contexts, they too
have components and these components, in turn, have still others.
A cell contains distinguishable parts with specialized functions, frequently referred to as organelles (Figure 4-2). Organelles are com-

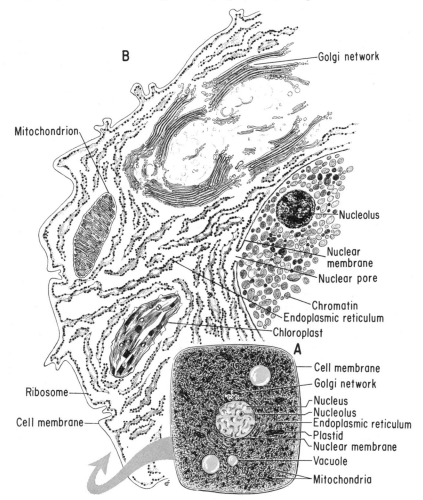

Figure 4-2. *Cell organelles in a portion of a cell (A) enlarged at (B).* [*From Abramoff and Thomson,* Laboratory Outlines in Biology, *1962, W. H.
Freeman and Co., San Francisco.*]

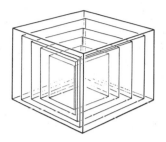 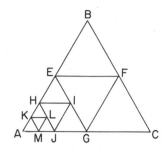

Figure 4-3. *Hierarchical order in Chinese boxes and subdivided triangles. Note that the triangle ABC is made up of four identical triangles, one of which is AEG. Similarly, AEG is made up of four triangles, one of which is AHJ. This triangle, in turn, is made up of four triangles, one of which is AKM.*

posed of structural elements—membranes, granules, amorphous materials. These structural elements can be separated into large molecular components, and the large molecules can be dissociated into smaller ones. Although the dissociation process can be carried on down to atoms, and even to subatomic particles, the realm of relatively large molecules is usually taken as the lowest biological level. Molecules, cells, organisms, and ecosystems are considered to be the major levels of the biomass, and any biological treatment is incomplete that does not take all of them into account. The biomass, functionally as well as structurally, can be thought of as an endless set of variations on the ancient theme of the Chinese boxes (Figure 4-3). In the hierarchy of triangular units, all units are identical except in size. In the biomass there is a similar hierarchical order, with at least several important differences: the units are very different, both between and within levels; the whole structure is dynamic rather than static; and the units are constantly interacting. Nevertheless, the relationships are similar in that ecosystems (ABC) are composed of organisms (AEG), which are composed of cells (AHJ), which are composed of molecules (AKM). The properties of the whole ecosystem are intimately interrelated with the properties of each subordinate level, down to the smallest.

To make this point concrete, imagine the following scene (Figure 4-4). A rabbit has been nibbling on the young shoots at the edge of a forest clearing. Suddenly, it takes alarm and leaps upward, only to

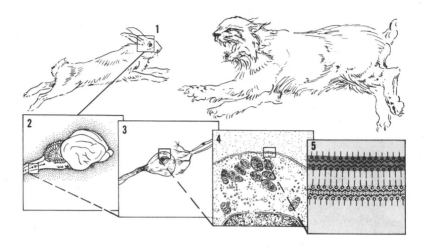

Figure 4-4. *Hierarchical order in a biological event, seen with increasing resolution. Levels: 1 = organisms, 2 = organs, 3 = cells, 4 = organelles, 5 = molecules.*

be met by a bobcat crashing down upon it. What is the best biological statement and interpretation of this event?

"Clearly," says the ecologist, "we are looking at a small sector of an ecosystem—specifically, a portion of a food chain which involves a secondary heterotroph (bobcat) catching a primary heterotroph (rabbit), in turn feeding upon an autotroph (green plant). Solar energy captured by the green plant is being transmitted and partitioned within an ecosystem."

"All true," says the organismal physiologist, "but let's get below the surface! Behavior is not just what you see in looking at the whole organism. Let's get some recording electrodes on that rabbit and find out what *really* is going on. Do you notice that volley in the sensory nerves just before his head goes up? It shoots right into the central nervous system, up the ascending tracts, through a relay in the hypothalamus, and radiates upward into the cortex. I don't yet know everything that goes on there, but somehow there is an integration of the incoming signals, and out comes a descending volley. It zooms down the spinal cord and out the motor neurons; the muscles contract and—leap! That's what really goes on during the split second of terror; you have to get down to the level of the nervous system to make real sense out of behavior."

Now the cell specialist moves in. "I see that you physiologists are still fussing with the complicated pathways of the nervous system. You'll never get to the bottom that way. Look for a short cut. Those neural pathways are chains of cells with switching devices at the junctions between them. What are the exchanges of substance and energy in these switches? Understand the cells and the switches and you have the key to the whole business."

"Actually," says the electron microscopist, "those junctions look pretty interesting, and may indeed be the key to intercellular communication. However, my electron micrographs show that they are probably only a special case of the general problem of the nature of cell surfaces. Certainly we are dealing with the same structural elements that are present in cell surfaces in general, and they look as though they are engaged in similar sorts of activity. I doubt that we will really understand the specialized and complicated neural junctions until we have a better idea of how the cell surface works in simpler situations. I'm concentrating on that and am finally beginning to get somewhere."

"That's fine," says the biochemist, "but you won't understand the operation of the cell surface—or any other organelle—until you know its molecular composition and behavior. You can talk about chains of cells and interactions between them, all you want, but it won't make sense until you know the behavior of these things at the molecular level. Actually, you know, the nervous system is a little unfavorable for studying this; much more progress has been made with muscle. Contraction was a mystery until it was shown that muscle contains the two proteins, actin and myosin, neither of which contracts by itself, but which in combination form fibers which can be made to contract. Once you have gotten a system like that into a test tube, you have a chance to learn something!"

"I agree," says the biophysicist; "with muscle we're finally getting close. Let me say, though, that we haven't yet discerned what really happens in contraction. There is a transformation of chemical energy into mechanical energy; presumably, energy-rich bonds are broken in some favorable spatial relation to chemical groups that can use the energy for coupling. However, the whole problem of energy transfer is a little complicated to follow in contraction, and probably is not fundamentally different from other situations that are easier to follow. For example. . . ."

The voices trail off, as we try to regain focus on the startled rabbit in his death leap. Do we understand him best as a primary consumer in the food chain of an ecosystem, as an organism in stress, as an assemblage of signalling devices and energized levers, as a community of cells with specialized organelles, as a collective of highly ordered, large molecules whose interactions involve energy transfers of extreme delicacy? Or do we need to choose among these alternatives? Is the rabbit equally describable and analyzable at all of these levels, and do we not require all of them for full conception? Like the three blind men who inspected the elephant, our investigators, applying themselves each at a single level, develop different conceptions of the rabbit. The leaping rabbit, however, is not their conception; it is the actual phenomenon. Each conception deals with an aspect at a particular level, and each has its advantage and disadvantage, depending on our purpose. Only in ultimate syntheses of all of the conceptions, including the elaboration of the interaction between the levels, will we recover the real rabbit.

What really happens as we investigate a complex process from its highest to its lowest level? We reduce the size of our field of observation and increase the resolution within it. We change our conceptual vantage point from our natural one among objects of our own size to other vantage points among objects of larger or smaller size. In discussing life and the universe earlier, we shifted our vantage point to conceive objects of much greater size than ourselves. We spoke of increasing orders of magnitude and saw the enormous range from the size of everyday objects to the immensity of cosmic distances. The earth, we said, is an object of ninth order. In these same terms, an ecosystem of moderate size might be about fifth order, and most organisms are first or second order. What orders of magnitude do we encounter as we focus on the suborganismal components of the biomass (Figure 4-5)?

Some muscles and nerves of a rabbit are readily visible without magnification; they are of order of magnitude zero. Others would be better seen under a $10 \times$ magnifier; they may be said to be of order of magnitude -1. The convenient unit of measurement at this level is the millimeter (25.4 mm = 1 inch). That a muscle is a bundle of filaments, laced together by connective tissue, would be

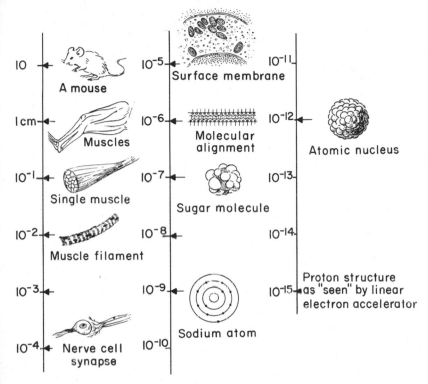

Figure 4-5. *Scale of decreasing magnitudes, from 10 cm (size of a mouse) to 10^{-15} cm (proton structure as "seen" by linear electron accelerator).*

best seen with a $100\times$ magnifier; muscle filaments are of order of magnitude -2. Generally speaking, cells (nerve cells, for example) are of order of magnitude -3, which is why their discovery awaited the optical microscope. The convenient unit of measurement at this magnitude is the micron (μ), one-thousandth of a millimeter. By and large, the resolution of the optical microscope is limited to order of magnitude -3 and is sufficient to distinguish cell parts, but not to appreciate their finer detail. The electron microscope resolves objects of orders of magnitude -4 and -5 and has made us aware of underlying structural regularity within cell parts. With it, for example, the relations between surface membranes at nerve cell junctions have been explored, and the altered spatial association of actin and myosin in contracting muscle revealed. In this range, the convenient unit of measurement shifts to the Angstrom (Å), which is one ten-thousandth of a micron. Objects of order of magnitude −5 do not include individual molecules, but the objects show patterns and shapes that directly reflect molecular alignment and packing. If we proceed to order of magnitude −6, just beyond good resolution of the electron microscope, we enter the world of macromolecules. Here the electron beam gives way to x-rays as the appropriate probe of structure. Moreover, molecules can be brought into solution to be examined by the techniques of the chemist. The smallest viruses lie in this range, and regularities based upon the arrangements of atoms in crystalline array begin to be noted. At order of magnitude −7, interatomic distances can be discerned in a salt crystal, and the backbone of a protein molecule is clearly visible. At order of magnitude −8 we are in the world of collections of atoms, and at order of magnitude −9 we can distinguish a single sodium atom. We need, however, to drop to order of magnitude −13 before the nucleus of the sodium atom appears at respectable size.

Ecosystem, organism, cell, organelle, macromolecule, molecule, atom, proton—these are units at the successive levels of resolution at which we may examine the biomass. It is important to recognize that successive levels differ not only in their units but in the mechanisms and distances of interaction among them. Below the biological realm, protons and other nuclear particles interact via the energy of nuclear fields (Figure 4-6), the nature of which we are just beginning to understand. Bonding interactions occur over distances of order of magnitude −13. Such interactions occur in nuclei of atoms within the biomass as well as outside it. We have no reason to think that there is any difference in the behavior of nuclei within and outside

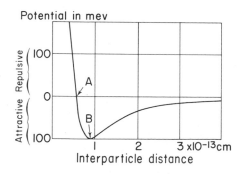

Potential in mev

Figure 4-6. *Nuclear force (measured in millions of electron volts) plotted against distance between particles. When the distance is less than at (A), the nucleons repel one another. They most strongly attract one another at (B).*

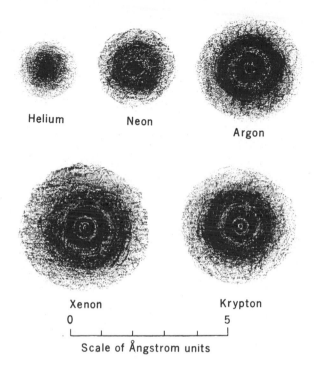

Helium   Neon

Argon

Xenon   Krypton

0   5

Scale of Ångstrom units

Figure 4-7. *Electron distributions in noble-gas atoms, showing successive electron shells.* [*From Pauling,* College Chemistry, *1964, W. H. Freeman and Co., San Francisco.*]

of the biomass; hence, we do not think of nuclear processes as biological. This does not mean that they are not biologically important. Their occurrence in expected form is essential to all biological reactions, and their departure from expected form—as in radiation effects—has profound consequences at all levels above the nuclear.

Intra-atomic interactions are largely electrical and occur over distances of order of magnitude −9. (Figure 4-7). They differ from nuclear reactions by many orders of magnitude, not only in distance but in the smaller amount of energy involved. They, too, are below the biological realm in that there is no known difference between the behavior of atoms within the biomass and outside it. Nonetheless,

atomic structure and its variations (in ionization or atomic excita-
tion levels) are, like nuclear processes, the substratum for higher-
level biological phenomena.

Atoms are bonded into simple molecules through interactions between outer-orbit electrons of neighboring atoms. This is the realm of
the chemical bond, involving distances that are of orders of magnitude
-7 to -8. As with nuclei or atoms, there are no interactions *peculiar*
to the formation of molecules of the biomass, though the frequency of
certain kinds of bonds (for example, hydrogen bonds) is far higher
than outside the biomass. Real differences between biomass and non-
biomass first appear at the level just above the simple molecules.
There is no essential difference in the character of the individual
interactions between simple molecules, but in the biomass, chain
formation among molecules is widespread, the links of the chain
being held together by repeated bonding of common kind. The formation of large molecules (polymers) by the linking of many smaller
ones (monomers) through like coupling reactions is known as polymerization (Figure 4-8). It occurs in nonbiological systems, but is of
spectacular frequency and variety in biological ones. Moreover, the
polymeric chains undergo folding, coiling, and looping to form struc-

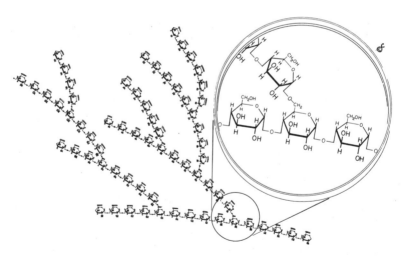

Figure 4-8. *Glycogen is a branching chain, or polymer, of many similar sugar molecules (monomers).* [*From Clark (editor),* Experimental Biochem-
istry, *1964, W. H. Freeman and Co., San Francisco.*]

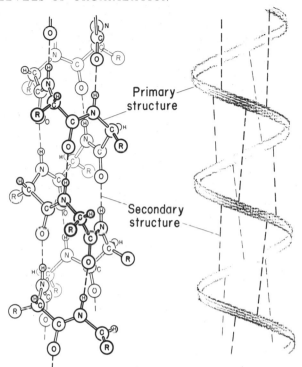

Primary structure

Secondary structure

Figure 4-9. *Secondary helical winding of a polymeric sequence of amino acids in a protein. The helix is maintained through hydrogen-bonding, as shown by broken lines. [From Clark (editor),* Experimental Biochemistry, *1964, W. H. Freeman and Co., San Francisco.]*

tures stabilized by intramolecular reactions (frequently, hydrogen bonding) along their length (Figure 4-9). Proteins are polymers of amino acids, nucleic acids are polymers of nucleotides, and carbohydrates are polymers of simple sugars. The nature and sequence of the monomers linked in polymerization determines the three-dimensional configuration of the chain, leaving certain units "buried" within the molecule and others "exposed" at its surface (Figure 4-10). The higher order interactions of the folded molecule will directly involve only the exposed portions of its length. If the nature and sequence of the monomers is designated as primary structure, and the folding of the chain as secondary and tertiary structure, it is clear that the reactivity of the molecule will depend on all three, but that

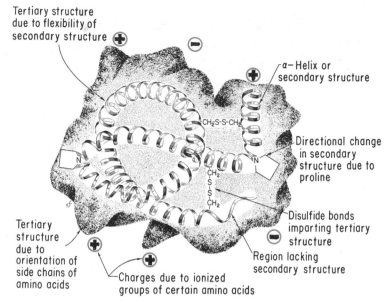

Tertiary structure
due to flexibility of
secondary structure

α—Helix or
secondary structure

Directional change
in secondary
structure due to
proline

Tertiary
structure
due to
orientation of
side chains of
amino acids

Charges due to ionized
groups of certain amino acids

Disulfide bonds
imparting tertiary
structure

Region lacking
secondary structure

CH₂S-S-CH₂

CH₂
S
S
CH₂

Figure 4-10. *Tertiary structure of a protein. Note that interactive properties (for example, charge and configuration) depend primarily on surface-exposed portions of complexly folded molecules. [From Clark (editor),* Experimental Biochemistry, *1964, W. H. Freeman and Co., San Francisco.]*

the tertiary structure will be particularly critical. Furthermore, since the tertiary structure is dependent upon bonds of lower energy than the primary, it will be more readily altered. The reactivity of biological macromolecules thus becomes peculiarly sensitive to environmental influence. Moreover, coupling reactions between such large macromolecules are frequently based on statistical summation of many weak surface properties (for example, patterns of charge distribution) rather than of specific interatomic linkages. The chemistry of biological macromolecules, therefore, differs somewhat in character from the chemistry of inorganic compounds, or even of smaller and simpler organic compounds.

The jump from macromolecular to cellular interactions is a long one, and we only dimly perceive as yet the kinds of interactions that may be involved in integrating the various cellular components. At the level where cells interact as units, however, it is clear that interactions can involve either the cell surfaces or the exchange of materials or energy across these surfaces. Once again, as in the secondary and tertiary structure of macromolecules, the possibility for direct interaction is limited to a portion of the total system—in this instance, to the surface or surface-controlled materials of the cell. In the next higher level of organization, the organism, the surface properties of the cells are crucially important. The surfaces are made up of macromolecular complexes, and hence show interactions characteristic of this realm. They can affect each other in important ways at distances of order of magnitude −5, the level at which macromolecular packing is the significant direct determinant of properties. Cells can also interact over much greater distances by the movement of materials from or through cell surfaces. Interactions of this kind are limited only by the amount, stability, and mobility of the materials being exchanged. In complex organisms there are arrangements which so facilitate material transfer that the range of intercellular interaction extends over the whole organism.

To reach the next major level we must again jump over a wide gap of ignorance about interactive processes. We know a good deal about the interactions of cells as subunits in an organism, but the full concept of all that goes on between cells in even the simplest multicellular organism still eludes us. However organisms may be integrated as cell collectives, they themselves tend to aggregate into groups, communities, and ecosystems. As in interactions at lower levels, these must again involve either the surface or the exchange of energies and materials across the surface. Interactions which integrate organisms into higher levels directly involve only a portion of the materials and properties of the organism, with heavy stress on the periphery. Reactions range from surface touch, through exchange of very simple to very complex substances, to the sophisticated energy-pulse communication signals of our own culture. Even if we exclude ourselves as a very special case, we find that organisms make use of a great variety of communication systems—systems that range from the electrically powered flashing of the firefly to the quasi-languages of higher mammals.

To recapitulate, there are characteristic units and modes of interaction at each level of organization in the biomass. In general, the units become larger and more complex at successively higher levels, and interactions between units place higher premium on surface or peripheral properties of the units. Interactions tend to take place over longer ranges at higher levels and to involve smaller amounts of energy per coupling. Although interaction mechanisms of lower levels may continue to operate at each higher level, new interactions appropriate to that level also appear. For example, the units of complex organisms interact via neural communication, which includes electrical and chemical components, but which clearly has its own new characteristics not displayed at lower levels. Thus, successively more complex units have successively higher order interactions. In this sense, the hierarchy of structure has its parallel in the hierarchy of functional control.

Reference

BERTALANFFY, L. VON
   Problems of Life. New York, Harper & Row (Torchbook TB 521), 1960.

Turnover
and
5   Continuity

Life conserves its properties, despite constant turnover of all components, through the ability to produce like from like at all levels.

There is a constant flow of energy and materials into, through, and out of the biomass. Nevertheless, the biomass persists as a whole, despite the continual turnover of the materials which compose it. At successive times the biomass may look the same, and it may contain the same numbers and kinds of organisms, cells, molecules, and atoms. But the individual components are not the same ones; some have moved out or have broken down, and others have moved in or have been newly formed. The materials and units are constantly undergoing turnover; the substance of the biomass is in constant flux. Components at each level are appearing and disappearing, but continuity of properties is preserved nonetheless. Like a candle flame, or a waterfall, the biomass endures despite the change of its components. In this chapter we shall focus on this remarkable property of continuity despite continual turnover.

Consider again the leaping rabbit at the edge of the forest clearing. We can go back to the forest year after year and find rabbits. In a given year, if we mark all of the rabbits in August and return in October, each rabbit we find will be marked. If we come back the following August, however, some rabbits will have marks and some will not. Ten years later, none of the rabbits caught will have marks. If we are sure that the marks were permanent on individual rabbits, we can conclude only that there is turnover of rabbits; some are disappearing and new ones are appearing. Over a ten-year period the properties of the rabbit population—color, size, behavior, and so forth—remain stable, even though its entire membership has changed.

The population of every kind of organism in the biomass shows turnover. The loss of members by death and dissolution is balanced by the production or formation of new members. Units at every level in the biomass are reproduced, though the mechanisms of reproduction vary with the level. Fundamentally, reproduction rests on replication; that is, *certain units have the capacity to make additional units like themselves.* Ecosystems, organisms, cells, and some molecules replicate under suitable conditions, and the duplication at any level involves duplication of each level below. Continuity of the biomass despite turnover rests upon replication of fundamental units. Turnover at each level is the product of coordinated replication at the level below. Turnover within populations is an expression of the replication of organisms; turnover within organisms is an expression of replication of cells, and so on.

To see this more clearly we can follow individual units from appearance to disappearance. We shall choose as a sample unit the organism *Escherichia coli* (*E. coli*), because it is simple and its mechanisms of continuity have been the subject of intensive and productive study. It is a bacterium found in the ecosystem that includes humans; in fact, in a sense it is part of the same food chain. By living in the human intestine, *E. coli* can partake of the by-products of human feeding. Ordinarily, it does not harm its host; the relation between the two is termed *symbiotic* (living together).

We can set up an artificial ecosystem involving *E. coli* by inoculating the organism onto an agar plate containing suitable nutrients (Figure 5-1). After a period of adjustment and increase, we can introduce a second organism, the slime mold *Dictyostelium discoideum.* The slime mold feeds on the bacteria. Theoretically, if we set up conditions properly, the number of bacteria can be held constant for at least a short period of time, because the rate of reproduction will be just balanced by the feeding rate of the slime mold. If we label the bacteria suitably at time T_1, we will find at a later time, T_2, that

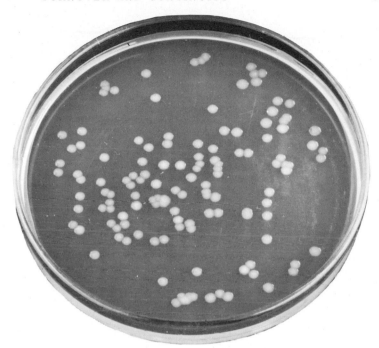

Figure 5-1. *An agar-filled petri plate on which individual bacteria have grown into macroscopic colonies.* [*From Stent,* Molecular Biology of Bacterial Viruses, *1963, W. H. Freeman and Co., San Francisco.*]

the number of labeled bacteria has decreased and the number of unlabeled bacteria increased. As with the rabbits, individuals are appearing and disappearing, yet the size and properties of the population remain constant.

Now let us follow an individual bacterium. It is a small, rod-shaped body a micron or two long, as seen under the optical microscope. To see detail, we need the electron microscope, which shows a thin peripheral capsule, or wall; a limiting external membrane within the capsule; a granular cytoplasm; and one or more fine fibrillar zones called nuclear regions (Figure 5-2). If we keep one of these tiny organisms in view for a half-hour or so, we will observe the following sequence, or cycle, of events. The bacterium will get larger for a while, increasing in wall material, area of surface membrane, and amount of granular cytoplasm and fine fibrillar material. Fol-

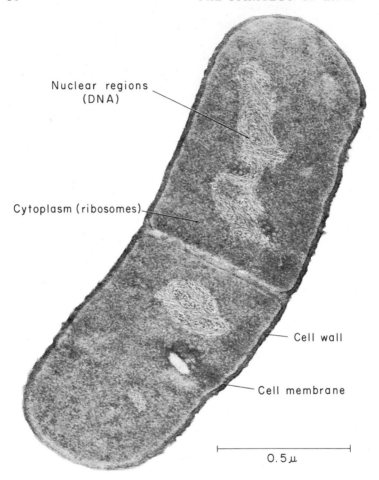

Nuclear regions
(DNA)

Cytoplasm (ribosomes)

Cell wall

Cell membrane

0.5 μ

Figure 5-2. *An electron micrograph of a section of a bacterium, showing the principal structural components of the eubacterial cell.* [*From Stent,* Molecular Biology of Bacterial Viruses, *1963, W. H. Freeman and Co., San Francisco.*]

lowing the growth phase, wall material will begin to form across the middle; this middle wall will become continuous and will double; and the original bacterium will divide into two parts, each of which contains a portion of the basic structures present in the original. This division process is known as fission and is the simplest form of organismal reproduction. Note that if each of the original bacteria in our artificial ecosystem were marked on its wall at one end, fission would yield one marked and one unmarked bacterium (Figure 5-3). Each bacterium now grows until it doubles its components, then fission occurs again. Of the four bacteria produced by the two

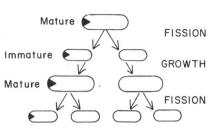

Figure 5-3. *Growth and division cycle of E. coli.*

fissions, only one will carry the mark. As the cycle, or life history, continues—growth, fission, growth, fission—the frequency of marked bacteria decreases. If we assume that the slime molds we introduced to feed upon the bacteria have consumed marked and unmarked bacteria at random, it is clear why the original population—which consisted entirely of marked bacteria—may maintain the same total number but show a dwindling number of marked members. There is turnover of the population, yet it has continuing properties because its individual members grow and replicate. The continuity of properties through generations of individuals is, of course, what we refer to as heredity.

Let us look into this situation just a little further. As the result of the last two decades of rapid progress in our understanding of heredity, we know that the fibrillar material seen in *E. coli* with the electron microscope provides the thread of continuity through the growth and fission cycles of bacteria, and almost certainly in all organisms throughout the biomass. The results of much ingenious experimentation reveal that the fibrillar material at the molecular level is, in large part, deoxyribonucleic acid (DNA), a long polymeric chain of four different but related monomers whose structures and relationships are shown in Figure 5-4. In any given organism, or strain of that organism, the four monomers, which we may call A, G, C, and T, occur in a highly specific sequence, as shown in Figure 5-5. An essential feature of each cycle of growth and fission is the replication or doubling of the DNA chain, followed by the equal partition of the products to the new offspring.

It is crucial to understand that the DNA is both replicated and involved, directly or indirectly, *in the production of all other new ma-*

terials formed during growth. Moreover, the properties of all new materials depend upon the specific sequence of monomers, which, in

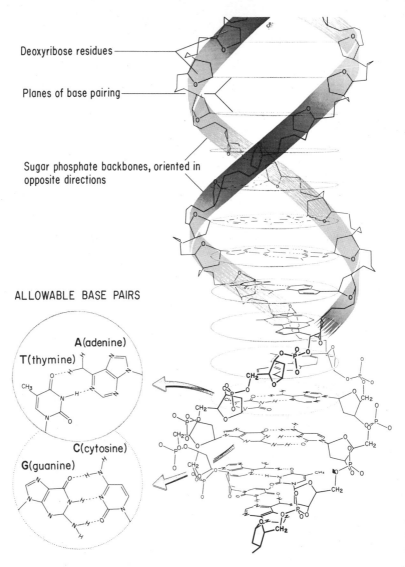

Deoxyribose residues

Planes of base pairing

Sugar phosphate backbones, oriented in opposite directions

ALLOWABLE BASE PAIRS

A(adenine)

T(thymine)

C(cytosine)

G(guanine)

Figure 5-4. *Strand of deoxyribonucleic acid (DNA).* [*From Clark (editor)*, Experimental Biochemistry, *1964, W. H. Freeman and Co., San Francisco.*]

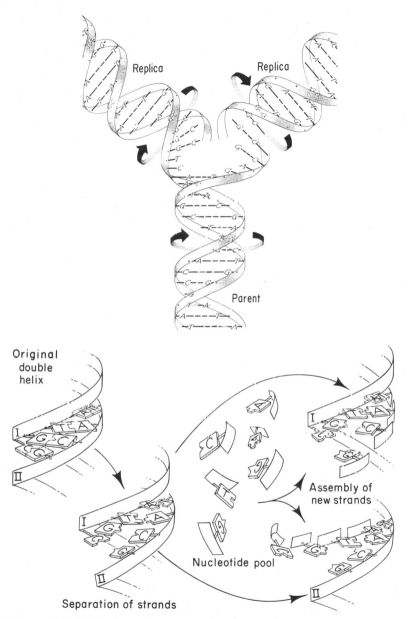

Figure 5-5. *Replication of DNA at the strand level (top) and at the nucleotide level (bottom). Note that the two complementary strands (I, II) of the original double helix each replicate a new complementary strand by assembly from the nucleotide pool.*

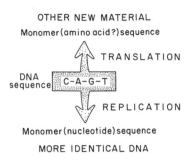

Figure 5-6. *Replication and translation of DNA in a reproductive cycle.*

turn, reflects the properties of the DNA as expressed in the sequence of nucleotides (Figure 5-6). Thus, in *E. coli*, replication of the whole organism is dependent upon (1) precise replication of its particular DNA and (2) control by the DNA of the properties of all other new materials, leading to replication of the total complex of properties of the parent. In the second step the relatively simple replicative properties of molecules are translated into the manifold complexity of a new organism.

We have referred to individual *E. coli* as organisms. We should emphasize that they are among the simplest organisms known. They do not, like more complex living things, consist of many cells. Rather each organism is at the level of a single cell; in *E. coli*, cell and organism are coextensive. Thus, in *E. coli*, the replicative properties of molecules are translated into properties at the level of the cell, which simultaneously are properties at the level of the organism. Let us now look further into how this occurs and point out at the same time the fundamental components of an organism (Figure 5-7). First, there is a replicative component (R), which we have identified in the fibrillar material of *E. coli*. The DNA of this material is the replicating molecule, but it is important to note that it cannot replicate by itself. For this it requires at least building blocks, or precursors; an energy source; and a catalyst, or enzyme. Provision of the energy and the enzyme (which itself is a protein and has to be synthesized by complex processes) is the business of the organism's second component, the metabolic component (M). Generally, the component M in *E. coli*, is the cytoplasm. Its functions, however, go considerably beyond the direct provision of energy and enzymes for replication. Energy and precursors must be captured from a varying environment, and the mechanisms for this are complex. Furthermore, materials involved in these mechanisms have to be synthesized by M. Whatever else M does, it must funnel its activities so as to feed R if the organism is to propagate, but R must guide M if propagation is to have continuity. Both components are indissolubly interlinked in the functioning organism.

Both R and M are made up of many interacting large molecules, and both the molecules and their delicate interactions are highly improbable in the general physicochemical environment. Component R is within M and interacts with the environment primarily through it. Component M, however, must be insulated to some degree as well, although it must be able to interact with the environment. The functioning organism has a third component—a boundary (B)—that sets it off from the general environment but which has properties concordant with the exchange requirements of R and M. Moreover, the three components, R, M, and B, and their subcomponents at the molecular level, are related to one another in special ways that are essential to the interactions among them and to the unitary behavior of the organism. One cannot produce an organism by mixing its components in a test tube; in fact, one destroys an organism by sufficiently disturbing its internal arrangement, even under conditions that do not directly alter its components. The rod-shaped *E. coli* are organisms not only because of the special nature of their components but because of the integrated fashion in which their components interact. We may refer to this aspect of the organism as I. We can summarize what we have been saying of *E. coli* as an organism in this way: *Each organism is a complex macromulecular system that behaves as a unit and is capable of replication through the conversion of materials and energies derived from the environment through a self-controlled interface or boundary.* The life history of *E. coli*, one of the simplest kinds of organisms, can be diagrammed to show the basic steps of biological continuity (Figure 5-8).

In order to make clear their fundamentally different significance and nature, replication and growth have been shown as separate phases in the diagram, though in fact they go on simultaneously in *E. coli*. Replication produces two identical replicative components, the essential step being the duplication of DNA molecules. The new

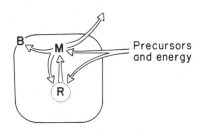

Figure 5-7. *Components of an organism as a reproductive unit.*

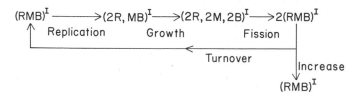

Figure 5-8. *Duplication of a basic reproductive unit.*

DNA is controlled in its formation by the old DNA; barring accident, there is no provision for modification. Growth doubles all of the other components of the organism through processes of synthesis guided by the DNA. Growth, however, involves incorporation of environmental energy and materials, and hence is subject to control and modification by their availability. Heredity (expressed in DNA) and environment interact in determining growth. When growth is completed, fission produces two new immature individuals. In Figure 5-8, one product is shown as replacing the original by turnover; the other is shown as constituting an addition. Both contain identical replicator components, and both are immature in that they do not have the ability to divide again immediately. Both must *develop* by growth—and perhaps in other ways—before they are mature.

The relatively uncomplicated life history of individual *E. coli* provides the cycle of turnover (with continuity) that characterizes bacterial populations in general. In simple plants and animals the situation is only slightly different. Let us look next at amoeba (Figure 5-9), which is a larger and more complex organism than a bacterium. Like *E. coli*, amoeba has no cellular components; rather, the organism is coextensive with a single cell. Unlike the fixed capsule of *E. coli*, an amoeba's surface is mobile, flowing, and capable of interacting with and engulfing materials from the environment. Its cytoplasm is far more complex structurally, and its functions are compartmentalized. Unlike *E. coli*, it has a distinct nucleus, with multiple chromosomes containing not only DNA but other materials as well.

Amoeba also has a replication and growth phase that doubles all components and is followed by fission. Fission of the cytoplasm is accomplished with no indication of strictly equal distribution of materials. The behavior of the nucleus, however, is far less haphazard; the remarkable process of mitosis (Figure 5-10) imposes a

high degree of precision. Each of the several chromosomes has previously doubled its materials and now splits *exactly* in half. An elaborate apparatus forms, partly from the cytoplasm, which ensures that
one-half of *each* chromosome goes to each product of division. The
regularity of the process emphasizes the crucial importance of the
replicative component. Nonetheless, despite the multiple character
of R (in several chromosomal packages) and the considerably greater
complexity of the other components, the amoeba's life history—and
its system of assuring continuity—is fundamentally similar to that of
E. coli and is equally well represented by Figure 5-8.

This is not true for the slime mold that we inoculated onto our
agar plates along with *E. coli*; part of its life history (Figure 5-11) is
similar to that of *E. coli* and the amoeba, but another part is importantly different. If we examine the agar plates during the phase
in which the number of *E. coli* still remains fairly constant even
though the slime molds are increasing, we find many individual
amoeba-like organisms moving over the surface and feeding on the
E. coli. Division takes place within these amoeba-like organisms in
the same way it does in the true amoeba. Replication and growth
alternate with fission, and the slime mold population increases in
number of like individuals. There comes a time, however, when the
E. coli population is depleted and the slime mold amoebae no longer
have a sufficient food supply. Their behavior then changes com-

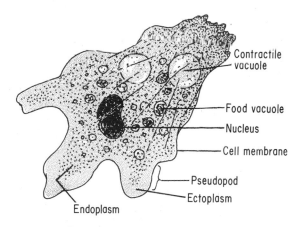

Figure 5-9. *Amoeba.* [*From Abramoff and Thomson,* Laboratory Outlines in
Biology, *1962, W. H. Freeman and Co., San Francisco.*]

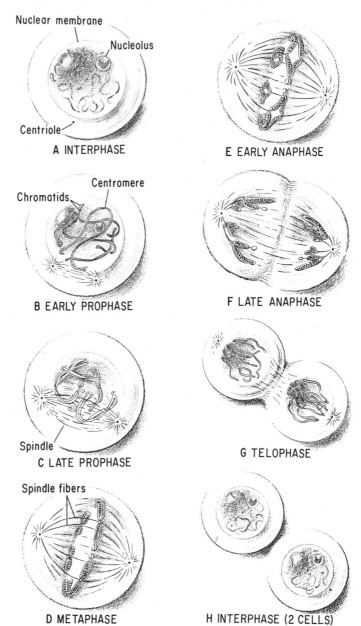

Figure 5-10. *Stages in mitotic division of a cell.* [*From Hardin*, Biology: Its Principles and Implications, *1961, W. H. Freeman and Co., San Francisco.*]

pletely. Instead of moving about randomly on the plate, they begin to "swarm" together into aggregates (Figure 5-12). These aggregates attract additional individuals, which flow in streams toward

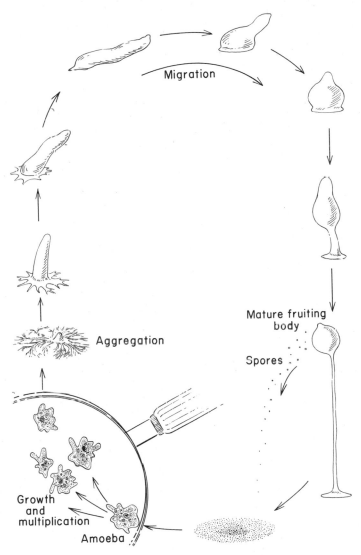

Migration

Aggregation

Mature fruiting body

Spores

Growth and multiplication

Amoeba

Figure 5-11. *Life history of a slime mold.*

them. The swarming produces a multicellular, slug-like mass. The slug, for a time, moves about *as a unit* on the agar surface. The activities of all of the individual amoebae in the slug are coordinated, or integrated, resulting in unitary behavior of the multicellular mass. This is shown in no better way than in the subsequent developmental history of the slug (Figure 5-11). After sliding about for a time, leaving a slime trail behind, it humps up into a hillock, becomes quiescent, and a stalk grows out of it with a round sphere, or sorus, at the top. This morphogenetic transformation of the slug is itself impressive, but more detailed examination shows something of further importance. Individual amoebae, previously all alike, have now diversified into several kinds (Figure 5-13). In the stalk, the amoebae have produced cellulose, the chief supporting material of plants, and have been rendered turgid by accumulation of droplets or vacuoles in their protoplasm. In effect, they are no longer individual organisms but specialized *cells* of a multicellular tissue. In the sorus, the amoebae have transformed into spores; their water content has decreased and they have developed a thick protective coating.

If we take some of these spores and inoculate them onto a fresh *E. coli* plate, the coating on each one splits and an amoeba comes out to begin feeding and propagating. The nonspore amoebae of the sorus, the stalk, and the basal disc die and undergo dissolution. Therefore, in this remarkable swarming and fruiting behavior in the life history of slime molds, we observe a multicellular phase in which cell-organisms begin to behave like components. Moreover, segregation, or differentiation, of the population into reproductive and nonreproductive units occurs. The reproductive units are the progenitors of the next generation, part of the continuous succession between generations, referred to as the germ line. The nonreproductive units nurture the germ line and contribute to its continuity, but are not themselves a part of it. The nonreproductive units may be referred to as the soma—the body cells (Figure 5-14). Note that although the body cells replicated as cell-organisms, they did not become part of the replicative component of the slug. Rather they are part of its M-component (as defined earlier for a minimal reproductive unit), since they are not themselves replicators but are essential for the effectiveness of the actual replicators, the spores.

The distinction between reproductive and nonreproductive cells becomes sharper when we consider such truly multicellular organ-

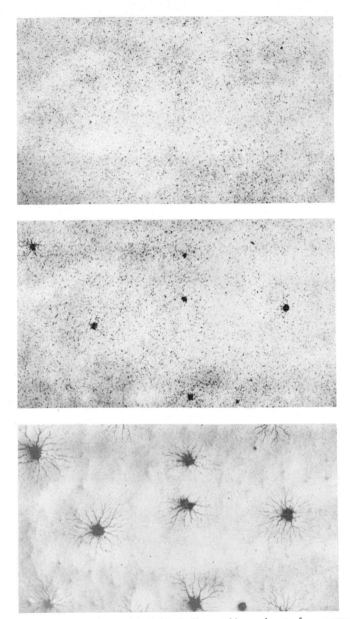

Figure 5-12. *"Swarming" of individual slime mold amoebae to form aggregates. (Top) Zero time. (Middle) Thirty minutes later. (Bottom) Ninety minutes later.* [*From Bonner,* Scientific American, *August 1963.*]

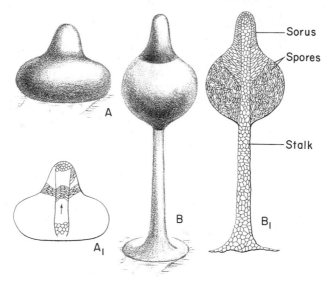

Figure 5-13. *Surface views (A, B) and sectional views (A₁, B₁) of two stages in the formation of fruiting structure of slime mold.* [*From Berrill*, Growth, Development, and Pattern, *1961*, W. H. Freeman and Co., San Francisco.]

isms as the rabbit. The adult rabbit is composed of literally millions of cells, which are specialized in many ways (Figure 5-15). As in the slime mold, there is a differentiation of reproductive and nonreproductive cells—the former are the bridge to the next generation, the latter die when the organism dies (Figure 5-16). Only a relatively small number of cells are reproductive, or germinal; the great bulk are somatic. The reproductive cells of the rabbit, of course, are not spores but gametes—cells that must fuse (into a zygote) to initiate a new individual. Moreover, the multicellular state of the rabbit does not arise as a result of swarming of many individual cell-organisms. In the rabbit, only the zygote can be thought of as a cell-organism. Within its organization, this cell contains all of the hereditary infor-

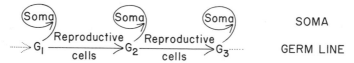

Figure 5-14. *Segregation of somatic versus germinal cells in multicellular organisms.*

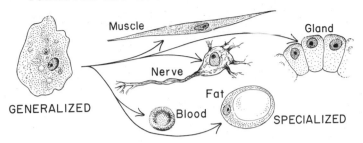

Figure 5-15. *Specialized cell types of the rabbit.*

mation needed to make another rabbit. When the rabbit zygote divides, however, its products do not separate as in bacteria or amoebae. They adhere and form a multicellular organism, like the slime mold slug. The developmental phase, which is relatively simple and short in *E. coli*, is long and complex in rabbits, and during development of the rabbit, the replicative molecular properties are translated into cellular and multicellular properties.

We have spoken of rabbits, slime molds, amoebae, and *E. coli* as organisms, and we have seen that the properties of each continue through generations, despite turnover of individuals, because successive generations of individuals are linked in time by replication. Since the whole organism is not directly replicated in all of its parts, this crucial operation originates in a molecular component whose properties then guide the new assembly or development of all the rest. *This is true of all organisms of all levels of complexity.* In cell-organisms (*E. coli*, amoebae), molecular properties are translated into organismal properties relatively directly. In organisms like the slime mold, which alternate between cell and multicell, molecular

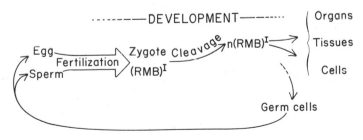

Figure 5-16. *Life history of the rabbit.*

properties are translated first into those of the cell phase and then into those of the multicell phase. The latter are a retranslation of the former. As the amoebae aggregate, their properties as individual organisms are amalgamated, altered, and integrated into those of the multicellular slug. In the rabbit, the highly complex multicellular organism must return to a cell phase to bridge the generations. The zygote contains its hereditary properties in its molecular replicator component. As the zygote divides, the fundamental replicative message is translated and retranslated in the developmental interactions of its growth and division. The properties of the new generation reappear as the hereditary message is transformed into higher levels of complexity. Regardless of the complexity of the organism, or of the biomass, its continuity in time rests on (1) an unbroken thread of replicative succession at the molecular level and (2) cyclic and often complex developmental translation of the replicated message during its life history.

Reference

LEVINE, R. P.
    Genetics. New York, Holt, Rinehart and Winston, 1962.

Continuity and Complexity

6

Continuity, despite complexity, flows by the production of like from like at the molecular level, followed by translation of molecular order through several levels of interaction until the full complexity of the mature organism is regained.

In the majority of organisms generations are linked by a cell phase, as has been described. However complex the organisms are as adults, reproduction is carried out at the cell level—either by gametes, as in the rabbit, or by spores, as in the slime mold. However, just as structure and function become enormously complicated in some organisms, so too does life history. For example, if the slime mold is cut in two, each half becomes complete and goes on to fruit normally. In many organisms this occurs naturally and regularly; the multicellular phase can multiply without return to the cell phase. This is spoken of as vegetative reproduction. It occurs widely in less complex multicellular animals and in plants. The phenomenon does not violate the stated principle; it merely reveals that the replicative message can be transmitted between generations in partially developed multicellular packages as well as in single-celled ones. Similarly, the life history of many organisms involves a series of relatively stable stages having very different properties. For example, one would hardly guess the caterpillar and the butterfly to be the same organism without seeing one develop into the other. Such a succession of unlike stages means that the replicated message may be translated in different ways at different times.

That complexity is not itself directly reproduced has been recognized only recently. For many centuries men disputed various explanations of the mystery of inherited complexity. Some argued that complexity must be formed anew in each generation. This view (called *epigenesis*) was acceptable in an age when belief in spontaneous generation and similar miracles was widespread. Believers in epigenesis were opposed by exponents of *preformation*, who asserted that the bridge between generations consists of a tiny but complete miniature of the adult. Naive epigenesis, on the one hand, provided little explanation for hereditary continuity and made development a recurrent miracle; on the other hand, naive preformation defined away the problem of development by propounding that miracle of miniaturization, the homunculus (Figure 6-1). Neither view in its naive and extreme form is acceptable now, but as so often happens in science, the current concept is a synthesis of the older and seemingly incompatible alternatives.

Figure 6-1. *Preformationism tucked a little man into the head of a sperm.* [Redrawn from Singer, A History of Biology: A General Introduction to the Study of Living Things, *1950, Schuman, New York.*]

Increased microscopic resolution discredited preformationism by revealing within gametes, not miniatures of the adult, but the modified organelles of a cell. But the question remained, what then *does* a hen's egg contain that leads it invariably to produce another chicken? Embryologists at the beginning of this century suspected that an answer might be found in the extreme orderliness observed in the early divisions, or cleavages, of the beautiful, translucent eggs of marine organisms. It was proposed that the regularly dividing nucleus contained developmental determinants that are parcelled

out to the various cells produced in the cleavage process. This modified form of preformationism did not involve a miniature, but it
assumed that all of the properties of the adult are present in the egg
as determinants and need only to be segregated out. In particular,
it assumed that the early divisions of the egg are of critical importance
in accomplishing this segregation.

Gifted experimentalists soon tested and settled this point. One of
the clearest early experiments was done on the salamander egg,
which is large enough to permit fastening a hair loop around it
(Figure 6-2). Pulling the loop tight confines the nucleus to one half
of the egg, and this half undergoes repeated division to produce 32
cells. Meanwhile the nonnucleated portion remains undivided. If
the loop is loosened at this stage, one of the cleavage nuclei can be

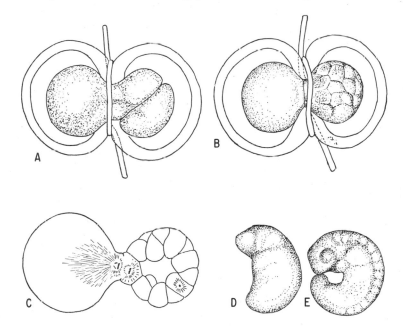

Figure 6-2. *Experiment to demonstrate nuclear equivalence following several cleavages. (A) Constricted egg with nucleus in right half, which has cleaved
once. (B, C) A nuclear cleavage product is allowed to return to the un-
cleaved half, as seen in the section at (C). (D) Embryo produced by the
right half. Development of (D) is delayed but normal compared with
that of (E).* [From Spemann, Embryonic Development and Induction, *1938, Yale University Press, New Haven.*]

released into the undivided half of the egg. By retightening the loop the egg can be constricted completely to yield two halves. The significant observation is that *both* halves will continue to develop normally; therefore, a single nuclear product of at least five cleavage divisions still has all the determinants necessary for complete development.

More recently, it has been shown that nuclei from cells considerably beyond the 32-cell stage still possess all necessary determinants for complete development. This can be demonstrated by transplanting nuclei from late-stage cells into fertilized eggs deprived of their own nuclei. In some instances it appears possible that even nuclei from differentiated cells that are already specialized in their functions may be able to be returned to the fertilized egg and to participate in all of the activities of a new course of development. Observations like these have virtually completely excluded the segregation hypothesis in its original form. Determinants are not parceled out as division occurs, but that is not to say that the nucleus does not contain determinants and that these may not function differentially in development. In fact, the evidence strongly suggests that they do.

Perhaps the most elegant demonstration of differential nuclear function is provided by the study of the giant chromosomes of certain insects. These chromosomes are giant because they are made up of many uncoiled strands in parallel alignment. The parallel alignment leads to cross-banding when the chromosomes are stained, because light- and dark-staining regions present on each strand lie adjacent to each other. The bands that stain dark prove to be richer in DNA. The important point in the present context, however, is that the chromosomes show a number of swellings along their length (Figure 6-3b, c). These "puffs," and the frequently associated "rings" of material external to the chromosomes, are present in different patterns (Figure 6-4) in the same tissue at different stages of development, and in different tissues of the same stage. The available information leads to the hypothesis that the swellings indicate DNA activity that is important to the synthesis of new materials. In these terms the differential pattern of swellings means that different nuclear determinants are active at different times and places. Determinants are not parceled out in cleavage, as was assumed earlier, but they are differentially active.

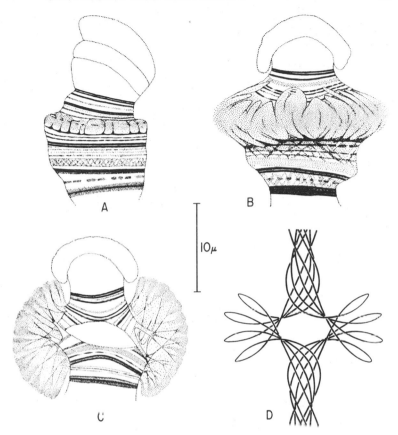

Figure 6-3. *Giant chromosomes and their puffing in salivary gland cells of the midge Chironomus. (A) Section of chromosome showing banding. (B, C) Increased degrees of puffing. (D) An interpretation of the behavior of individual chromosomal fibers in a puffed region.* [*From Bonner and Ts'o,* The Nucleohistones, *1964, Holden-Day, San Francisco.*]

What establishes the pattern of differential activity? Two general hypotheses are possible. Either the pattern is built into the genic system (the genome) itself or it is imposed in whole or in part by stimulus and control factors impinging upon the genome from outside. In one hypothesis (independent genomic function) the developing organism is comparable to an old-fashioned player piano, in which a master tape of instructions specifies every note as the tape is

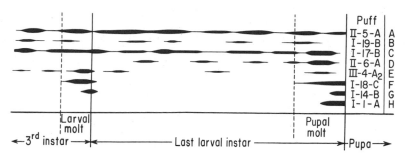

Figure 6-4. *Pattern of puffing in different chromosomal regions at successive stages in the development of the midge. The progression of stages is indicated in the lower part of the diagram; the individual chromosomal regions, to the right. Note the variation in thickness of the lines representing puffing activity.* [*From Bonner and Ts'o,* The Nucleohistones, *1964, Holden-Day, San Francisco.*]

played through from end to end. In the alternative hypothesis the developing organism is comparable to a piano on whose keyboard extragenomic factors play, usually eliciting familiar melodies but on occasion evoking previously unheard tunes—or even unmelodic noise.

A final choice between the alternatives cannot yet be made; the question is just beginning to be approached by investigative procedures likely to prove decisive. One thing, however, is clear: as in the earlier controversy over preformation and epigenesis, the answer may combine elements of the two alternatives. However long the sequences of notes that can be played by tape may be, the piano certainly has some keys that can be pressed from outside the genome to establish which part of the tape is to be played at a given time. Perhaps the proper analogy is not the piano but the modern juke box, which can be instructed from without as to what record or sequence of records to feed in and then plays each record automatically and mechanically until it is completed.

What is the evidence that the genome is not entirely self-instructed? Experiments on sea urchin development bear on the point. The sea urchin is closely related to the starfish, and its egg is a clear spherule containing a broad band of cytoplasmic pigment granules that can be used as a landmark to orient the egg. When the band is horizontal and the larger, unpigmented zone lies above it, the egg corresponds in orientation to the larva it gives rise to (Figure 6-5). Cleavage and reordering of the cells of the original zygote follow a regular pattern, as though nuclei and their contained genes had to function according to a built-in pattern. If we disturb the pattern, however, we find that this is not so. If we cut the unfertilized egg (Figure 6-6) into halves, parallel to but just above the pigment band, the halves quickly round up and heal; each can be fertilized by a sperm. Both halves cleave and, regardless of which half contains the egg nucleus, the half without the pigment band develops into a small incomplete ball whose cells look like those of the upper half of the normal larva. The half with the pigment band also develops into an incomplete ball, but its cells and structure resemble those of the lower half of the normal larva. It appears that in halving the unfertilized egg we have in some sense halved the larva.

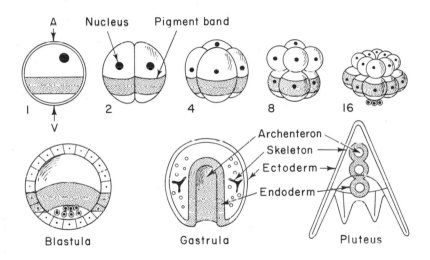

Figure 6-5. *How the contents of the egg may be traced into the embryo (pluteus). Top, left to right: The egg (A = animal pole, V = vegetal pole); 2-cell, 4-cell, 8-cell, and 16-cell stages. Bottom, left to right: Section of a blastula with the cells from the vegetal pole entering the cavity of the blastula; section of a gastrula with the archenteron; section of the pluteus with the pigment band localized in the gut. [From Barth,* An Introduction to Embryology, *copyright © 1953, Holt, Rinehart and Winston, Inc., New York.*]

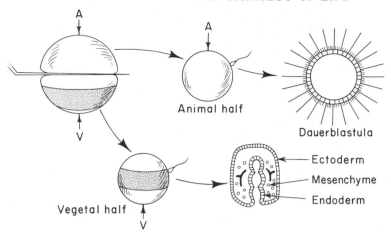

Figure 6-6. *The development of animal and vegetal halves of the sea urchin egg. The egg is cut in two through the equator by means of a glass needle. The animal half (top) is fertilized and develops into a blastula (dauerblastula) but fails to form endoderm. The vegetal half (bottom) after fertilization forms an incomplete embryo.* [*From Barth,* An Introduction to Embryology, *copyright © 1953, Holt, Rinehart and Winston, Inc., New York.*]

A different result obtains, however, if we cut an unfertilized egg perpendicular to the pigment band (Figure 6-7). On fertilization, each half produces a larva that is complete though somewhat reduced in size. Therefore, everything necessary to produce a complete larva is contained in half the egg when it is cut perpendicular to the pigment band, but not when cut parallel to it. From these findings we derive two conclusions. First, the cytoplasm of the egg is not homogeneous; materials significant for development are localized to some degree, and thus normal development occurs only in a part that contains at least a portion of all of them. Second, equivalent sperm nuclei introduced into each of the three kinds of halves (upper, lower, or lateral) function in three different kinds of development. Thus, the assumption is that the behavior of the nucleus differs in these three situations; its behavior cannot be programmed entirely internally, but must depend in part upon the nature of the cytoplasm in which the nucleus resides.

By extension, we conclude that although important determinants for development lie in the zygote nucleus, the cytoplasm of the zygote is not simply a blank page on which the nucleus prints out instructions. The history through which cytoplasm has gone in the earlier development of the ovum has already made it significantly heterogeneous, and it is with this cytoplasm that the nucleus interacts. The strength of some cytoplasmic determinants has been shown in the various eggs that produce what is known as a polar lobe. For example, the fertilized egg of *Dentalium* (Figure 6-8) is largely pigmented, but there are two clear caps of cytoplasm at the poles. The plane of first cleavage passes through both poles, dividing the clear cytoplasm of the upper pole. The clear cytoplasm at the lower pole, however, segregates in only one cleavage product, or blastomere, because it protrudes as a lobe to one side of the cleavage plane. At second cleavage the polar lobe of clear cytoplasm reappears, and once again the material segregates in only one cleavage product.

The polar lobe of clear cytoplasm makes a very special contribution to the developing egg, though its precise nature is not known. If the lobe is snipped off at first cleavage the egg develops abnormally, forming a small plate of ciliated cells. If the lobe is snipped off at second cleavage the egg develops into only the upper half of a larva. Moreover, when eggs are exposed to elevated temperatures before first cleavage, polar lobe formation is altered; some of the clear cytoplasm passes to each cleavage product, and twinning results, each product of the first cleavage becoming a complete embryo.

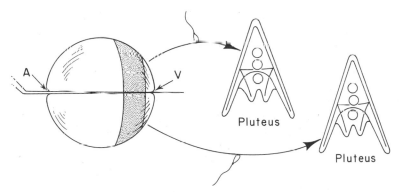

Figure 6-7. *A sea urchin egg is cut in two through the animal-vegetal axis, A–V. Each half is fertilized and each half develops into a normal embryo of half size. [From Barth,* An Introduction to Embryology, *copyright © 1953, Holt, Rinehart and Winston, Inc., New York.]*

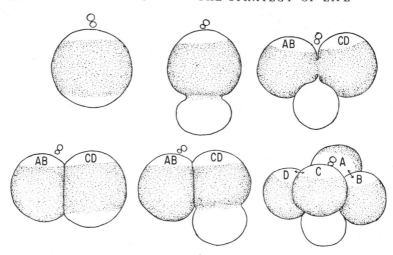

Figure 6-8. *Cleavage of the egg of the mollusc Dentalium. A "polar lobe" forms before first division and this material is returned into CD but not AB. A lobe appears again at the second cleavage and the material returns into D. [From Fig. 1, Wilson, J. Exp. Zoology,* **1**:*6 (1904).]*

Clearly, development here involves more than the simple imprinting of nuclear instructions on the cytoplasm; the cytoplasm has its own developmentally significant properties. The products of nuclear activity, transcribed and translated from the genome, must interact with cytoplasmic materials to yield retranslations and amplifications as the egg grows and diversifies.

Nucleocytoplasmic exchange is a primary interaction in the developmental reading of the genome. There are, however, successive interactions beyond this in all multicellular organisms. This is readily demonstrable in the sea urchin embryo. As the zygote cleaves,

Figure 6-9. *Formation of the lens in the axolotl. In A the superficial cell layer of the embryo is thickening where it is associated with the optic vesicle. In B a small vesicle is produced which separates from the superficial layer in C. D, E, F show enlargement and differentiation of the vesicle into a lens as the eye matures. None of the events of lens formation will occur if the optic vesicle is removed. [From Spemann,* Embryonic Development and Induction, *1938, Yale University Press, New Haven.]*

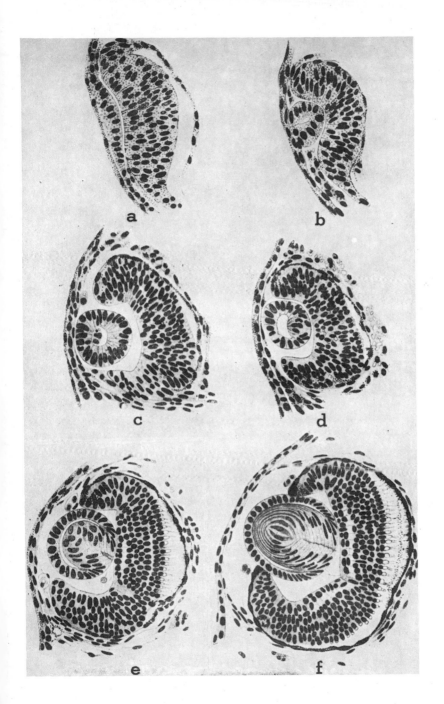

a

b

c

d

e

f

the products remain as an aggregate instead of separating into individual cell-organisms as they do in such unicellular forms as amoeba. As cleavage progresses, more and more cells are produced and these become more and more different one from another. Differentiation implies specialization of form and function and, in turn, differential activity of the genome. Although the mechanisms underlying the adhesion of cells as aggregates are not fully understood, they can be disrupted experimentally. Exposing early sea urchin embryos to sea water deficient in calcium and magnesium reduces the adhesiveness of their cells and causes the cells to separate. If they are returned immediately to normal sea water, the cells reaggregate and continue developing normally, which indicates that the deficient sea water does not damage the cells so they cannot develop. Nonetheless, if the disaggregated cells are returned to ordinary sea water but are not allowed to reaggregate, they fail to continue development and specialization. Some kind of interaction that takes place between cells in the aggregated state seems to be important for their normal behavior in development.

At the next level of organization, the important developmental influence of cell aggregates, or tissues, upon one another is one of the best-documented products of developmental analysis. Tissue interaction begins very early in the development of vertebrates—for example, with the establishment of the central axis of the embryo. It also plays an essential part in the formation of the eye, where the lens forms normally from the superficial layer of the embryo only if the rudiment of the remainder of the eye comes into proper association with the superficial layer (Figure 6-9). In fact, this kind of interaction operates in the early stages of formation of every organ that has been appropriately studied. In each organ the direction of development and specialization of one group of cells is controlled by its association with another; that is, the function of the genic complement in the cells of the group is directed by its associations with its neighbors.

In later stages, development is importantly influenced by hormones in plants and animals and by neural influences in animals. In still later stages, the organismal environment also can directly or indirectly, influence genetic translation. Thus, the genetic message passed from generation to generation is translated and retranslated as successively higher levels of complexity emerge during development. The existence of these successive interactions and translations makes possible control of the properties of organisms through manipulation not only of the genome (genetics) but of its mechanisms of expression (development) as well.

Variation
and
Diversity

7

The diversity of life is built upon the variation provided by degrees of error in the replication of molecular messages; it is the consequence—and the record— of the interaction of life and earth.

So far, we have characterized the biomass as a highly heterogeneous system, whose components undergo turnover without changing the overall properties of the units of which they are a part. This is a fair characterization if we limit our observations to time intervals of not more than a few generations of the most rapidly reproducing organisms within the biomass. If we watch the biomass for a longer period, however, we become aware that there are slow changes in its properties, and in the properties of its constituent organisms.

These changes can be appreciated on two general time scales. The paleontological record tells us that the character of the biomass has changed during the course of earth's history (Figure 7-1). If we were able to enumerate fully the kinds of organisms present at each of two widely separated time planes, the evidence indicates that the lists of organisms would not be the same. Some kinds of organisms present at the earlier time would not be present later, and vice versa. Moreover, it can be demonstrated that there has been sequential change in the properties of some organisms (Figure 7-2) over a period of time. Organisms of a later time may be traced back, in a series of identifiable steps, to organisms of an earlier time. We generalize this by saying that kinds of organisms are constantly evolving within the changing biomass.

During short intervals of time, within the span of laboratory investigations, propagating organisms show changes of properties that can be followed in detail. Mice, for example, which breed very rapidly for higher animals, can be watched through about 25 generations in a decade. They can be bred entirely by brother-sister mating so as gradually to minimize hereditary differences. Brother-sister mating produces strains whose members are all genetically as close as identical twins (the products of a single zygote). Both in identical twins and in these highly inbred mouse strains, pieces of skin can be grafted from one member to another without any evidence of the incompatibility and rejection that ordinarily occurs in grafts, even between members of immediate families. However, if one divides a colony of inbred mice and breeds each half as a separate subcolony for a decade, it frequently happens that skin grafts can no longer be made successfully between members of the two subcolonies. Despite continued brother-sister mating within each, in the course of 25 generations the two substrains diversify sufficiently to lose their tissue-graft compatibility.

Hereditary changes that appear over a decade in mice can be demonstrated even more strikingly in a much shorter time with *E. coli*. This organism can go through 50 generations in a day, and its

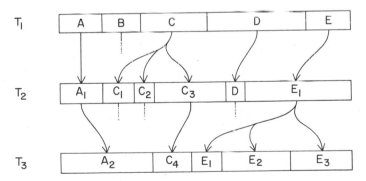

Figure 7-1. *Changes in the species composition of the biomass at successive time planes (T_1, T_2, T_3). Species A to E are hypothetical.*

properties can be examined in terms of simple and readily analyzable processes such as nutrient uptake from the environment. For example, by using proper procedures, one can very quickly produce strains that either do or do not utilize the sugar, galactose, as a source of energy. One can start with a single bacterium and, in a matter of weeks, derive from it a variety of strains, each distinguishable by its requirements for various nutrients, and each propagating its particular characteristics in successive generations.

Thus, both the paleontological record on a long time scale, and laboratory and other breeding experience on a short time scale, lead to the conclusion that duplication of units of the biomass is not as completely invariant as our earlier discussion implied. For restricted numbers of generations the dominant note is strict replication, but for larger numbers of generations, variation from strict replication becomes increasingly important. Indeed, if we examine the matter very carefully we find that even within one generation there are variants, but the number is so small that for certain purposes we can effectively neglect it. To an understanding of long-term changes, however, this low-level variation is of crucial importance.

We can detect the presence of these variants only by very special methods. Within a population composed of a strain of E. coli that cannot use galactose to grow, there are always a few members that can use it. If the strain is put on a galactose-containing medium that is poor in other energy sources, these few members will, through their continued propagation, become the dominant members of the population as those that do not use galactose die out. Appropriate tests show that the bacteria that can utilize galactose do not appear as soon as galactose is made available, but are produced at a low rate by the bacteria that cannot use it.

How can this be? For the answer we must return to the subject of molecular replication (Figure 7-3). We saw earlier that duplication of the long-chain polymer, DNA, underlies the propagation of like

---

Figure 7-2. *Change with time in characteristics of the horse. Note "main line" from Eohippus to Equus, "offshoots" to Hypohippus and Hipparion. Only molar teeth and front feet are shown.* [*From Kummel,* History of the Earth: An Introduction to Historical Geology, *1961, W. H. Freeman and Co., San Francisco.*]

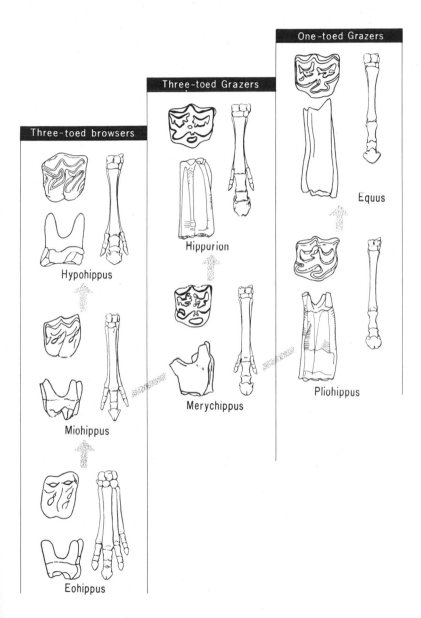

Three-toed browsers

Hypohippus

Miohippus

Eohippus

Three-toed Grazers

Hipparion

Merychippus

One-toed Grazers

Equus

Pliohippus

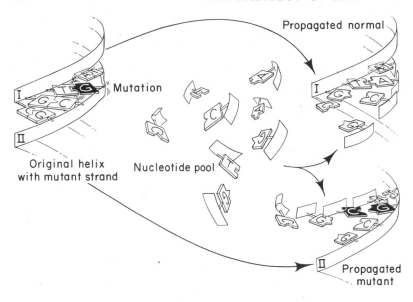

Figure 7-3. *Propagation of a mutation by "error" (substitution of G for A) in a DNA strand (II). Compare with Figure 5-5B. Once the error is made, replication will propagate it.*

properties from one generation to the next. We noted that the critical property duplicated is a fixed sequence of monomers of four kinds, and that this sequence is translated into all other hereditary properties. Clearly, the transmission of hereditary properties between generations is dependent upon the accuracy with which the sequence of monomers is duplicated. If a "mistake" is made in the duplication process, the transmitted message and all of its translations will be altered. Mistakes can be conceived to be of various kinds and degrees of seriousness. For example, a large section of the message might be omitted, or it might be so garbled that it could not be translated at all. Then the offspring receiving it could not complete their development and could not produce offspring in turn. So large an error, therefore, would not be propagated; it would be eliminated in the very organisms in which it occurred.

A somewhat smaller error, equivalent perhaps to a typographical error that transposes two words in a sentence without obscuring the meaning, might be replicable and translatable but produce an organism of reduced effectiveness—for example, in utilizing an environmental energy source such as galactose. Such an error might be propagated in the population for varying periods of time, depending upon the degree of reduction of effectiveness and the availability of the environmental energy source. If the organism carrying it were put at a serious disadvantage in relation to the original organism, the error would disappear quickly, particularly if both were in competition for the same energy source. If the energy source were abundant, however, the error might make no difference at all, and both the original and the variant versions might propagate indefinitely. One would become aware of the error only if a change in the availability of the energy source put a premium on the original message.

Of course, there is also the possibility that some errors *improve*, rather than impair, the effectiveness of an organism. Indeed, if two versions of the same portion of the message exist in the population, one cannot say without additional information which is "correct" and which is "erroneous." This is particularly true when we consider that changes in messages are frequently reversible; that is, a transposition of two message units can occur in one direction and then in the opposite. The important point to note is that, through minor failures of its machinery, the duplication process allows variation to be introduced into the fundamental messages. Inaccuracies in the duplication of messages are called mutations. Because the basic messages are expressed in molecular order, and their alteration involves the kinds of factors that control molecular assembly, the nature and frequency of mutations depend on physicochemical rules rather than biological ones. Not all mutations are simple "copy-errors"; many involve more complex changes than we shall discuss here. All, however, are recognizable because they give rise to altered translations, or phenotypes, which propagate the new message. The frequency of any given mutation (site of error) is low, but *the overall mutation rate is high enough to maintain a significant number of nonstandard members of various kinds in even the most carefully controlled population of organisms.*

Important consequences flow from the regular occurrence of this kind of mutational error; any propagating population may contain a reservoir of variants, and the differential propagability of these provides a mechanism by which the properties of the population can adjust to the conditions of particular environments. Consider a population of bacteria in the vicinity of a hot spring (Figure 7-4). The

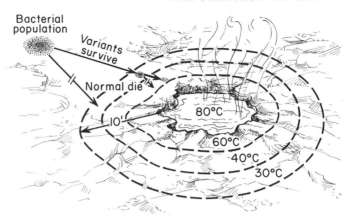

Figure 7-4. *Successive invasion of a hot spring by heat-tolerant variants of peripheral organisms.*

temperature at the orifice of the spring may be 80°C, grading away peripherally to ordinary temperatures 10 feet away. Most bacteria are excluded from the entire area by their sensitivity to temperatures over 30°C. If a population contains a few variants that are less sensitive to high temperature than the rest, they may infect the 30°C zone, there finding "open territory" for their growth. Having "colonized" the 30°C zone, the population will continue to produce variants, some of which may be even more tolerant of high temperatures. Eventually, some variants may be produced that will colonize the 40°C zone, thus extending the population into yet another area. The fact is that thermophilic (heat-loving) bacteria are found *in* the waters of hot springs, existing under conditions that seem inconceivable for life. It seems reasonable to suppose (although it has not been proved) that the selective, more rapid reproduction of mutational variants gave rise to this unusual form of life. The interaction of hereditary variation and differential reproduction of variants, depending upon environmental characteristics, is what has been called natural selection. Through natural selection, lineages of organisms are *adapted* to particular niches of the biosphere, and continue to press into new ones.

Hereditary, or genetic, variation provides a mechanism that not only enables the components of the biomass to adjust to new environments, and hence extend the biosphere, but enables the biomass to adjust to slow changes in the properties of the biosphere. A bacterial population exposed to a slow rise of mean temperature from 20°C to 30°C will behave in time very much as it would if it were invading a new 30°C niche in space. The variants that can tolerate higher temperatures will multiply more rapidly than those that cannot, and will maintain the population under the new conditions. There is an important difference, however, between occupancy of a new spatial niche and occupancy of what we may call a new temporal one. Around the hot spring, bacteria of various degrees of temperature preference may survive and propagate in some zone. Adjustment to a change of environment, however, may in time change the whole exposed population, and its original properties may disappear altogether. When environmental change is continuous and progressive, as has been the case on the earth's surface, the adjustive changes in the biomass are equally progressive and, with time and accumulation of change, will become irreversible.

The process already described—adaptation to environment by differential reproduction of random variants—accounts for the heterogencity of the biomass and indicates its profound significance. Given a nonuniform and changing environment, life's response is the production of many kinds of organisms, each adjusted to a particular part of the environment at a particular time. To appreciate this, think of a homogeneous biomass composed of only one kind of organism. Such a biomass might remain homogeneous if: (1) the environment were entirely uniform and unchanging or (2) the single kind of organism were able to survive and propagate over the entire range of environmental variation in space and time. The first condition certainly does not correspond with the earth as we know it now, nor does it correspond with any period in our reconstruction of its history. The second condition seems very demanding, particularly since there would have to be built into the homogenous biomass provision for survival not only in the existing range of environments but in all future possibilities. In these terms, homogeneity seems improbable; replicative heterogeneity is the fundamental "strategy" the biomass uses in dealing with the contingencies of environmental variation. It follows, interestingly, that today's heterogeneity must be interpretable as the consequence—and the record —of the adjustment of the biomass to all past contingencies. Diversity of the biomass as we know it is the product of its long interaction with the biosphere, a continuing interaction whose fundamental mechanism is self-duplication of units—a self-duplication based directly or indirectly on replication of molecular messages, but subject to certain degrees of error.

References

DOWDESWELL, W. H.
    The Mechanism of Evolution. New York, Harper & Row (Torchbook 527), 1960.

EHRLICH, P., AND HOLM, R.
    The Process of Evolution. New York, McGraw-Hill, 1963.

Progression
and
8   Complexity

*First, replication and variation
provided a living substrate; then
increased size, complexity, and
phenotypic adjustment permitted a new
range of freedom and movement
within the environment.*

We have seen that the biomass is heterogeneous and changes with time, and that its diversity—the result of constant adjustment to changes in the biosphere—protects its future. Given progressive change in the biosphere, there will be change in the biomass. We illustrated this with examples from the behavior of bacteria and saw that the reaction mechanisms of bacteria are sufficiently effective to adapt them to new environments. But now we have another and most intriguing characteristic of the biomass to deal with. The biomass does not consist entirely of relatively simple units like bacteria, although they occur virtually everywhere in the biosphere. Rather, in addition, we find units of far greater complexity than bacteria, and these complex organisms behave in ways far beyond the capacities of the simpler ones. What has driven life to higher levels of organization? Since bacteria are successful in adapting to a changing environment, why has the biomass produced such complex organisms as mice and men?

Flushed with enthusiasm for the recent progress in biological investigation, it is easy for us to forget how much we do not know. We cannot, for example, give full or even partial answers to the questions posed above. But if we cannot answer fully, we can at least approach the problem, inventory it and set it against the background of what we do know, and perhaps provide a useful target for further investigation.

As a preliminary step, of course, we should be sure that we really have a problem. Perhaps life has not moved from lower to higher levels of organization; perhaps it began with prototypes at various levels, each of which has replicated—occasionally producing variants —ever since. The fossil record goes back less than a half-billion years, to the rocks of the Early Cambrian period. As old as they are, these rocks contain fossils of most of the major types of organisms; the prototypes of all but the vertebrates and higher plants made their appearance in the biologically almost-unplumbed Precambrian period. We have no direct evidence of the way in which organisms higher than the cell level might have originated, and we do not know what advantages multicellularity may first have conferred.

Despite these gaps in our knowledge, we have grounds for believing that progression from lower to higher levels did occur during the history of the biomass. For instance, our knowledge of complex organisms as they exist today convinces us that they must have arisen from pre-existing organisms; we can no longer accept the hypothesis that complex organisms arose de novo under any conditions we can imagine on earth. If the antecedent organisms were themselves complex, then they must have come from outside the earth, but this hypothesis becomes less and less attractive the more we know about the inhospitable conditions for life in interplanetary and interstellar space. Moreover, to assume an extraterrestrial origin would only place the problem farther out of reach (at least for the present); we would still have to explain how life originated, wherever it did. At the same time, we now see more and more clearly how conditions on the earth may have once favored the appearance of macromolecules and their association in simple organisms. Evolutionary progression from simple to complex organisms is currently an enigma, but as our knowledge grows it looks as though it would be easier to make sense of progression than of any other hypothesis for the origin of complex organisms.

Further, the problem of progression to higher levels is now less awesome, because we realize that every complex organism that develops from a spore or a zygote goes through exactly this transition from lower to higher levels of order. The fact that this transition can be made in each short life history makes it credible that transition of a comparable sort was made in the biomass over its long history.

There are instances among the probable lineages of existing kinds of organisms in which evolutionary transition from level to level can be documented. Moreover, it appears to have occurred a number of times in different lineages, and not only from cell to multicell, but from organism to multi-organism. We shall take the time to describe an example at each of these levels.

The organism *Chlamydomonas* (Figure 8-1) is a green unicell,

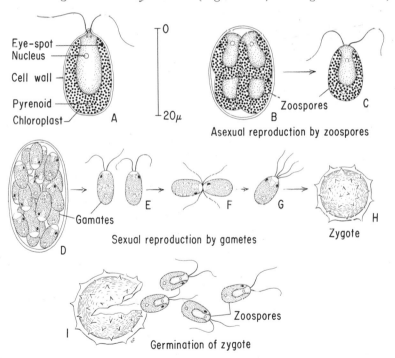

Figure 8-1. *Structure and reproduction of the green alga Chlamydomonas.* [*From Hardin*, Biology: Its Principles and Implications, *1961, W. H. Freeman and Co., San Francisco.*]

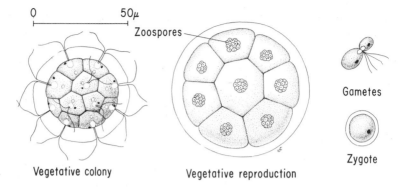

Figure 8-2. *Structure and reproduction of the green alga Pandorina.* [*From Hardin,*
   Biology: Its Principles and Implications, *1961, W. H. Freeman
   and Co., San Francisco.*]

approximately like amoeba in complexity, but different in detail. It
is an autotroph, and it swims about by means of a pair of whip-like
flagella. Its life history involves the same fundamental cycle of growth
and mitotic fission as has been described for amoeba, but with the
additional feature that this organism sometimes undergoes several
divisions without compensating intervening growth. The resulting
cells of reduced size behave as gametes: they fuse to form a zygote,
which then renews ordinary growth and division. Except for the
period immediately following division, the organism is always a unicell when in sufficient water, and each of these organisms is like
every other in its ability to reproduce by simple division or to undergo gamete formation. When growing on damp soil, however, offspring produced by division sometimes fail to produce flagella and
may remain embedded in gelatinous, amorphous colonies of thous-
ands of cells. When the mass is flooded with water, individual cells
develop flagella and swim away.

The closely related *Pandorina* (Figure 8-2) has individual cells very
similar to those of *Chlamydomonas*, but these regularly occur in clusters
of fixed cell number and arrangement. The number of cells in the
cluster varies from 4 to 32, depending upon the species. In asexual
reproduction each cell divides to form a new cluster, and these are
liberated by dissolution of the common matrix. In sexual reproduction each cell divides to form gametes, and these are released to

swim about until fission occurs. Unlike *Chlamydomonas*, the *Pandorina* gametes are of two sizes, though otherwise of similar structure. In *Eudorina*, another organism essentially similar to *Pandorina*, the size difference between gametes is even greater, and the larger gamete is nonmotile. The smaller gamete is liberated from the male parent colony and penetrates into the female colony to fuse with one of its cells and form a zygote.

The sequence of increasing cell number and specialization of gametes reaches its culmination in *Volvox* (Figure 8-3). This is a spherical colony of 500–40,000 Chlamydonomas-like units embedded in a matrix and interlinked by cytoplasmic strands. Only a limited number of these units, in one region of the colony, are able to give rise to new colonies either sexually or asexually—that is, only some of the component cells are germinal; most are somatic. In sexual reproduction, certain cells in a female colony enlarge to form a definite egg. The enlarged egg-cell is fertilized by motile cells, which swim to it through the water and the gelatinous matrix of the female.

A *Volvox* "colony," with its cells of specialized function, is not easily distinguished from a simple multicellular organism, and it is no wonder that many biologists regard the *Volvocales*—the group to which all of these algae belong—as a possible model of how multicellular organisms arose. Whether or not the model is accurate in detail, this series (and others like it that might be described—for

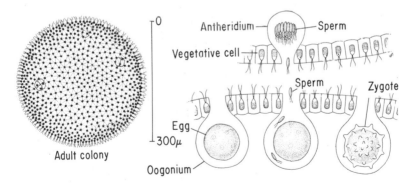

Figure 8-3. *Left. A single Volvox individual. Right. Portions of male and female individuals are shown at greater magnification. Note sexual reproduction and the production of a zygote.* [*From Hardin*, Biology: Its Principles and Implications, *1961*, *W. H. Freeman and Co., San Francisco.*]

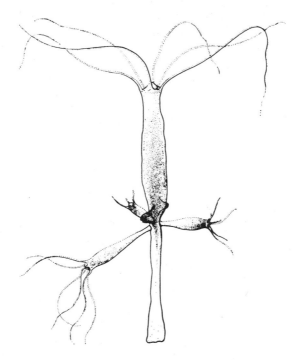

Figure 8-4. *Hydra undergoing budding to form new individuals.* [*From Berrill,* Growth, Development, and Pattern, *1961, W. H. Freeman and Co., San Francisco.*]

example, in the ciliated protozoa) shows that organisms above the level of cells *can* form from the failure of unicells to separate.

Equally striking is the fact that similar phenomena occur at the next higher level—from multicellular organism to multiorganism. For an example we turn to the relatively simple animals known as the hydroids. The prototype, *Hydra* (Figure 8-4), consists of a multicellular hollow shaft fixed to the substrate by a foot or base. The free end of the shaft is equipped with a mouth and a surrounding circle of tentacles. The organism can reproduce either sexually by the transformation of certain cells of the shaft wall into gametes or asexually by folding of the wall of the shaft outward to form a bud. After a period of growth and development, the bud separates at its base to yield a new individual. Sometimes separation is delayed until a second, or even a third, bud begins to form and, for a time, the organism seems to be multiple.

Obelia (Figure 8-5) is a colonial hydroid in which nonseparation of buds is typical. From a common branching tube, or stolon (which persists as a supporting and communicating structure, not unlike the

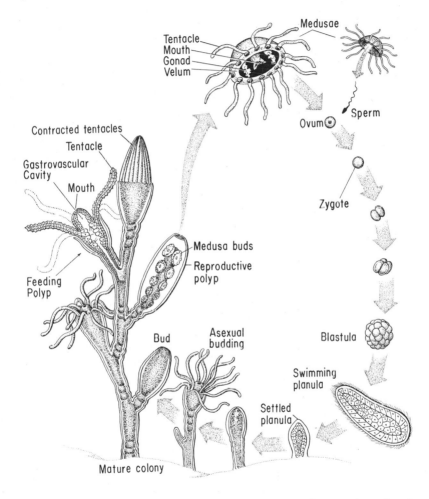

Figure 8-5. *Life History of the colonial hydroid Obelia.* [*From Abramoff and Thomson,* Laboratory Outlines in Biology, *1962, W. H. Freeman and Co., San Francisco.*]

trunk and limbs of a tree), the buds form two kinds of individuals, or polyps. One kind of polyp is very much like *Hydra* in structure and behavior; it carries out all of the functions of the colony except reproduction. The second kind has no mouth or tentacles, but it buds off new individuals from its walls. These new individuals are not polyps but small medusae, or jelly fish, which swim about and eventually produce gametes. The gametes fuse to yield a zygote, which in turn forms a new polypoid generation. Thus, the hydroid colony consists of multicellular units, some of which are specialized for reproduction and others for somatic functions.

Hydractinia (Figure 8-6) is another colonial hydroid. It has

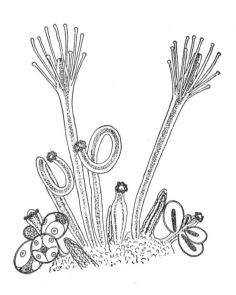

the interesting habit of growing as a mat on snail shells that have been taken over by hermit crabs. Its stolon, like *Obelia's*, gives rise by budding to hydra-like polyps and reproductive polyps—and to a third kind as well. In *Hydra* and *Obelia* the tentacles are equipped with stinging cells that paralyze and help to capture prey. In *Hydractinia* one type of polyp is specialized to carry an abundance of stinging cells, leaving the other two types to concentrate on feeding and reproduction, respectively. The reproductive polyp does not produce free-swimming medusae; instead, gametes are produced right in the wall of the polyp.

Figure 8-6. *The colonial hydroid Hydractinia, enlarged to show the several forms of polyp.* [*From* The Invertebrates: Protozoa Through Ctenophora, *Libbie H. Hyman, copyright © 1940 by McGraw-Hill Book Co., New York.*]

The process of specialization of polyps within a colonial mass is carried still further by *Physalia*, the well-known Portuguese man-of-war (Figure 8-7). Only by watching the early development does one become aware that the large, delicate float is a specialized polyp, and that this polyp is derived from a stolon that gives rise to at least four other kinds of specialized individuals. Long, thin, stinging polyps hang as a curtain of tentacles below the float. A fish paralyzed by these tentacles is drawn up to the shorter, feeding polyps, which are interspersed among reproductive polyps and blade-like protective polyps. Without knowing something about its development and relationship to other colonial hydroids, no one looking at *Physalia* would guess that it is not a single organism. Indeed, even knowing these things does not make it easy to categorize it either as organism or colony. If it is to be thought of as an organism, its multicellular "organs" are modifications of a level of organization that also occurs in independent organisms, just as the cell-organs of *Volvox* are modifications of cells that can occur as independent organisms.

Figure 8-7. *Physalia, the Portuguese man-of-war. The large float is a modified polyp, as are the several kinds of tentacles dangling below.* [*From* The Invertebrates: Protozoa Through Ctenophora, *Libbie H. Hyman, copyright © 1940 by McGraw-Hill Book Co., New York.*]

The foregoing examples are intended to show that progression from one level of complexity to another has occurred during the history of the biomass, and hence that it is not unreasonable to assume that all organisms of higher level may have been derived from organisms of lower level. One might object that both examples involve relatively simple organisms and that conclusions based upon these examples may not be applicable to more complex ones. But

Figure 8-8. *An idealized scene in a termite colony, emphasizing the extreme differences in size and function among the members. The central figure is the reproductive termite, or queen. [From Richards,* The Social Insects, *1961, Harper & Row (a Torchbook), New York.]*

the fact is that colony formation very similar to that of the relatively simple hydroids occurs in several other groups of organisms—including the tunicates, which we suspect of being close to the line from which vertebrates came. Moreover, something comparable occurs among the insects, which are among the most complex of invertebrate organisms.

Members of a termite colony are not, of course, linked by anything like a stolon; each member is a physically independent organism. Nonetheless, they live in colonies, and their biological continuity can be ensured only by the collective; the individual termites are specialized into a number of structural and functional types (Figure 8-8). Only the winged, reproductive members are able to produce gametes, and they can do this only if they are fed and cared for by other members of the colony. There are several varieties of nonreproductive members; some with large mandibles for fighting, others that carry on the work-a-day activities, and still others that can become substitute reproductives in the absence of primary reproductives. The number of different kinds of individuals produced in the colony at a given time depends upon interactions among the components and upon conditions within the colony. The propagation of the colony is the direct activity of the reproductives, but the degree of their success depends upon the activities of all of the specialized members and upon the characteristics of the colony.

Hence, if we can generalize our examples (and most biologists believe that it is reasonable to do so) we can say that there is, and has been, a strong tendency in the biomass toward ever higher levels of organization. But we still must ask: What is the driving force? What leads life to higher orders of aggregation and complexity?

The finding that aggregation is a persistent property of all matter under appropriate conditions* provides a beginning, but it does not make clear why higher and higher levels of bioaggregation do, in fact, occur. Neither does it rationalize the particular kinds of higher order aggregations of living forms nor tell us how continuing aggregation and increasing complexity gave rise to properties so very different from those of the nonliving world that they were long thought to be "nonmaterial." The attempt to clarify this leads us to look at the possibilities and limitations of the several levels of biological organization and to ask in what ways higher levels might increase the possibilities and reduce the limitations of lower levels.

One thing is clear immediately. We can conceive of a world populated by bacteria; we cannot conceive of a world inhabited only by vertebrates or only by trees. Complex organisms depend upon simpler ones for their support; ecosystems invariably include simple

---

*Discussion of aggregation and biological complexity has often been confused by the suggestion that this kind of behavior of the living world conflicts somehow with the second law of thermodynamics. The inviolable second law asserts that isolable systems of matter and energy move toward increasing randomness rather than toward increasing order; the entire universe moves toward randomness from the point of view of its energetics. Life, however, is not an isolable system, and the second law does not exclude increasing order in *parts* of systems, even in the nonliving world. Atom-building goes on in the stars; local ordering is accompanied by radiation of enormous quantities of energy outward, and this energy increases disorder (thermal agitation) elsewhere. Atoms condense into molecules in the cooler stars, and molecules condense to crystals on the planets. Minerals, rocks, geologic strata represent successively higher levels of aggregation in the nonliving world. Increase of order is not unique to life, nor is it precluded thermodynamically in parts of any system. The second law says only that with increasing order at one point, there must be decrease at some other point, and overall, the decrease outweighs the increase. Viewed thermodynamically, the biomass is a phenomenon of intense local ordering—self-directing and rapidly spreading, improbable but clearly not impossible as long as the price is paid elsewhere. For life on earth, it is the sun that pays the price through its steady thermonuclear combustion of hydrogen. Were life and its manifestations not "thermodynamically possible" life would, of course, simply declare the second law impossible!

as well as complex components. Higher levels of order in the biomass do not replace lower levels; whatever the advantage gained by increasing order, it does not wipe out the lower levels. Rather, various levels of order coexist in the biomass as part of diversification, which is, as we have observed, a major factor in life's strategy for dealing with varying environments.

What limitations to diversification would there be in a biomass composed entirely of bacteria? It is not easy to imagine the character of such a biomass, but consideration of the question emphasizes how much the nature and distribution of existing bacteria depend upon other organisms, particularly complex ones. We have said that bacteria exist virtually everywhere in the biosphere at the present time; in many places, however, bacteria are there only because other organisms are there. For example, bacteria are present within most other organisms as commensals or as parasites. They "ride" their hosts into many regions, rather than invading them by themselves. We are today concerned that earthly bacteria may accompany our rockets to the moon or Mars, contaminating them and spoiling our chances of collecting reliable evidence of their biotic history, if any. But bacteria would not be expected to find their way from earth to a lunar niche by themselves. Further, many bacteria depend upon the abundant oxygen of the atmosphere, which would not exist except for the metabolic activities of the higher plants. Still others survive only where there is a supply of decaying material from higher organisms to feed upon. If we could eliminate all of this, and also make allowance for other tricks that bacteria might devise to make a living from other bacteria, can we say how large a biomass they might compose and what fraction of the existing biosphere they might inhabit?

Although it would be difficult to answer this question for the entire earth, it is not unanswerable in principle; it might be approached experimentally in limited areas, for example, particularly in artificial ecosystems. It would be interesting and important to know the conditions under which the introduction of more complex organisms increases the productivity of an ecosystem. For the moment, the question serves to emphasize a context in which the significance of complexity might profitably be approached: What new properties are conferred upon the biomass by higher levels of organization? Does more complex organization remove some limitations to the increase of the biomass, and allow extension of its occupancy of the biosphere?

The first limitation removed would, of course, be size. Individual bacteria are invariably small; the simplicity of the procaryotic (pre-nuclear) bacterial cell must be size-limiting, though in ways that cannot yet be detailed. The more complex eucaryotic (truly nuclear) cell, which is found in organisms other than the bacteria and blue-green algae, achieves much greater size. Bacteria reach a micron or two in length; algae and protozoa achieve sizes one and even two orders of magnitude higher. In some fashion, sharper delineation of the nucleus and increased structuring and compartmentalization of the cytoplasm makes greater size possible. *Greater size is in itself a significant new property,* since larger organisms can feed upon smaller ones by engulfment. In the presence of small organisms occupying an environment even to their fullest extent, larger organisms can still evolve to live as predators upon the smaller ones. Size increase thus achieves further diversification of the biomass.

Beyond this, however, eucaryotic organization at the cell level provided the opportunity for the development of replicating units of still greater size through complex and delicate interactions within a mass of cohesive cells functioning as subunits. Bacteria occur in aggregates and colonies, but the degree of interaction within these aggregates remains minimal; they behave as piles of organisms rather than as multicells. Eucaryotic aggregates do not behave as mere piles; their individual units interact and exchange so effectively that some can concentrate on one thing and some on another, to the common service of all. Specialization of subunits within the aggregate, accomplished through differentiation, welds the mass into an effective unit of higher order. The achievement of this step created a whole new size range—from the tiny rotifer to the massive whale.

As size increases, a new consequence readily becomes apparent. We have seen that genetic diversification is a basic strategy for dealing with environmental variation. Small organisms generally have a short generation time; they can rely on existing genetic variants, and the rate of production of new ones, to cope with environmental change, because genotypic variation is quickly translatable into phenotype. Large organisms, by comparison, necessarily have a longer generation time; it takes longer to put them together. The effectiveness of genetic diversification as an adjustment device is reduced in large organisms, at least in the ratio of the generation times of large and small organisms. In man, the time span between generations is some 500,000 times longer than in *E. coli*. Were there not some other device for adjustment, man would be at a profound disadvantage relative to bacteria in dealing with environmental change.

The alternative device was mentioned earlier, when we considered the significance of heterogeneity of the biomass. Adjustment to environmental change can be achieved either by alteration of the frequency of genetic variants in a population or by alteration of the properties of individual organisms. It is interesting to note that these two alternatives would be expected to be oppositely affected by increasing size. Greater bulk means longer generation time, but it also means more "internal environment," more components, and more machinery for coordination. By coordination we mean internal communication; that is, the transmission of messages within the system. From components sensitive to messages within the system, it is a relatively short step to components sensitive to external information; that is, to environmental change. Hence, increased size also means increased potential for environmental regulation. Organisms that are large and complex, relative to the small, simple ones we have discussed in some detail, represent a most pregnant further diversification of the biomass. They allow the biomass to explore phenotypic adjustment for coping with the environment as a device to supplement genotypic heterogeneity. By coupling organismal processes directly with environmental cues—by means of coordinating systems with peripheral sensors—the biomass acquires the ability to extend the biosphere by entry into, and adjustment to, environments forbidden to simple replicative units.

Considered in terms of the simplest replicator—the molecular one —each new level of organization provides a new degree of freedom in at least two senses. First, it is another shell of insulation of the replicative process from a potentially unfavorable environment. We have seen that replication is fundamentally molecular, and dependent upon a fairly narrow range of physicochemical conditions. The first requirement of an organism is to provide these conditions, and to maintain them in whatever general environment the organism encounters. The organism does this through mechanisms generally designated as homeostatic; that is, in the face of varying environments it undergoes alterations that minimize the consequences internally. The more deeply the essential replicative machinery is "buried" (the more levels of control between it and the environment), the more likely that the critical conditions for replication will be preserved.

Second, each new level of organization is a new translation of the basic molecular message, and opens a new world of opportunity for expansion of the biomass, both quantitatively and qualitatively. The basic message is molecular, a sequence of only four kinds of units. Given a long enough chain, an enormous amount of information can be carried, since each addition quadruples the previous possibilities: 4, 16, 64, 256, ... If, however, these chains had to cope with the environment directly—if the various DNA's were thrown out naked on the surface of the earth—relatively few changes of sequence of their subunits would modify their properties significantly for even their chemical survival. It is not naked DNA but DNA clothed in complexity that has made its way in the world! It is in the translation of altered sequences of DNA into altered properties of proteins and other materials—into phenotype— that DNA variations begin to acquire significance. *Small molecular variations become crucial when they are translated into the properties of propagating biological units.* The properties of bacteria already represent several levels of translation, through which molecular properties are expressed at the level of organization of a procaryotic cell. Small molecular changes—for example, the shift of a single subunit of DNA—can, under certain conditions, make very large differences in the amount and kind of biomass. The consequence of molecular change is enormously amplified in the process of translation. Eucaryotic organization introduces still higher levels of complexity even within the cell units. When these aggregate to multicells a new context is created. Molecular properties, previously translated to cell properties, are now once again turned into an entirely new language, that of a multicellular organism exquisitely coupled with its environment. When such organisms aggregate, whether by physical continuity in hydroid colonies or close interaction in insect or human societies, still another context and language is achieved. Each time translation occurs the molecular message acquires a new degree of freedom; each translation affords creative opportunity in the interaction of message and environment.

We began this chapter with the question: What drives life to higher levels of organization? We have not fully answered this question, but we have seen that the answer is closely tied to the nature of life itself. Replication leads to variation, and variation leads to heterogeneity and genetic adjustment to varying environments. Genotypic adjustments provide a substrate of living substance on which diversification can build further. Increased complexity comes with increased size, and the two together permit phenotypic adjustment. Phenotypic adjustment affords a new range and freedom of movement within the environment. And we end with more questions: Is progression driving on to still higher levels? Where does progression and complexification of the biomass lead?

Reference

WALLACE, B., AND SRB, A. M.
    Adaptation. Englewood Cliffs, Prentice-Hall, 1961.

Direction
and
9   Intelligence

*Awareness of the future and capacity
for choice, newly appearing with Man,
increasingly challenge him to supply
direction and purpose; conscious
Strategy of Man is a necessary sequel
to the Strategy of Life.*

In closing, we cannot fail to note that the biomass recently produced a new, dominant species—man, a complex organism existing in further complexes, or societies, involving a high degree of coordination at this new level. With mounting size and integration of his social complexes, man increasingly has affected other species, both directly and indirectly, by changing the biosphere. In very recent time it has become clear that the existence of the biomass itself could conceivably be determined by the activities of man. This situation is new, but like all biological innovation it has its antecedents and its continuity with all that has gone before.

We have spoken of the biomass as existing in the biosphere, as though one existed within the other and the two were sharply bounded at an interface. This, of course, is an oversimplification. Organisms also exist within organisms, as we have seen; in a sense, the hosts are biosphere for their parasites. The tree is the ecological niche for nesting birds, and it provides essential cover for shade-loving ferns. The oxygen of the earth's atmosphere, essential to so much of the biomass, is the product of some of the components of the biomass. The geochemical activities of the biomass have, in part, *created* the characteristics of the biosphere, and the interaction between the two continues.

Beyond this, many organisms supplement their internal adjustment by controlling their immediate environment. We saw that adaptation can involve mechanisms of phenotypic regulation that minimize the internal consequences of environmental change (homeostasis). An obvious extension is to minimize the chance of environmental change by cutting off a section of the general environment and controlling it. This can be done either by internalizing a portion of the environment—as we do in the air passages of our lungs or the lumen of our gut, both of which are continuous with the outside— or by rearranging it so as to isolate a portion, as a bird does when it builds a nest in which its eggs can be kept warm. The biomass extends the biosphere not only by self-modification, so as to be able to invade new niches; it also extends the biosphere by modifying the environment in ways that adjust it to the requirements of the biomass.

This process of environmental modification is seen in simple organisms, but it is particularly impressive among more complex ones, especially animals. By and large, bacteria and plants spread into suitable environments and slowly adjust to them; animals more actively *invade* environments and alter them to fit their own activities. Corals build reefs, within which individual polyps have a relatively constant environment. Tube worms form their own chambers, within which they can lie protected while feeding on organisms brought into the chamber by water currents that the worms themselves produce. Bees (and other social insects) build nests—sometimes of astonishing complexity—within which the complicated and integrated behavior of many individuals provides a continuous food supply, community protection, controlled temperature, and other advantages. Increasing complexity of the biomass is accompanied by increasing degrees of environmental control, both by capturing and internalizing the environment and by manipulating and rearranging it externally. In these ways the environment is organized or directed according to the pattern of the living organism; the biomass is a director of the nonliving and utilizes the nonliving to suit its needs.

These statements raise problems that we must face squarely if confusion is to be avoided. A bird picks up strings and sticks and piles them in the crotch of a tree. We explain that it is organizing its environment to protect its young. Embryos do not yet have homeostatic control of their body temperature, so their immediate environment must be kept warm even though the temperature of the environment falls during the night. The parents sit on the nest and convert it into a little incubator. The birds "make arrangements" to protect their young at a later time.

Are the birds acting with purpose? Do they know that the female will soon lay her eggs, and that there will be young birds who will need protection? Almost certainly not. The birds are responding to a series of cues, some internal and some external, that lead to nest building. This behavior has a long history in the species; we only dimly understand its nature and origin. We assume, though, that behavior has evolved, like the size, shape, or any other structural characteristic of the species, as the result of genotypic variation and the differential reproduction of variants that best fit the environment. The birds do not behave as they do because they know the future, but because the past experience of their species has been built into their behavorial patterns. They are organizing their environment because their progenitors who did this were successful in producing offspring, which, in turn, did the same. In these terms, direction of the environment is no different from any other adaptive property of the biomass; it is part of its strategy for dealing with external inconstancy. Among the mechanisms that have proved successful are those that extend *into the environment* the homeostatic constancy of the organism.

Good enough. Now what can we do with man? Here is a director and arranger of the environment at a new level. He not only manipulates sticks and strings, he even rearranges the lives of many of the other species within the biomass. He learns to do tricks with fundamental energy sources and has the power to alter the properties of the whole biosphere. On the one hand, he tinkers with molecular messages that underlie the entire fabric of life; on the other, he stands ready to step off the earth and lead a boarding party to other planets. Is all of this, also, without foreknowledge or purpose? Is man merely a mechanism for extending the biosphere? Is intelligence no more than a homeostatic device, operating externally to improve the effectiveness of the biomass in its drive to extend the biosphere? Could such a device operate antithetically to lead not only to self-destruction of man, but to destruction of the entire biomass?

These are questions whose implications go beyond biology. In certain contexts it is useful to regard man as a mechanism for extending the biosphere and to regard his intelligence as a mere homeostatic device. We can view man's entire culture as a controlled portion of the environment—sticks and strings arranged to fit man's pattern of living. We can even assume that man has no conscious foreknowledge or purpose (for we really do not know that anyone but ourselves has, and we are not always sure of ourselves). In certain contexts we may so view man; in others we cannot. When we focus on human society in all of its complexity we recognize that man and his culture —although stemming from and building upon all of the experience of the biomass—represent a level above all the rest; that man is something more than "a mere mechanism to extend the biosphere." In human culture a further retranslation of molecular, cellular, and organismal messages has occurred, and another degree of freedom has been achieved. In man we see, as has so often been seen before in the history of the biomass, a "new" phenomenon.

Above all else, the human level is characterized by awareness of future and the capacity for choice. Between the two—for the first time on earth and possibly in the universe—a component of the biomass can *consider* the direction in which to turn. It remains to be seen to what degree products of such consideration and deliberation can become factors in events; that is, whether human purposes and desires can become conscious planners and movers of the universe. Man has long assumed purpose in the universe—a purpose that he has personalized in a Divine Being. Man now is challenged to provide purpose himself, since science is placing in his hand increasing power to control events and hence to implement purpose. Science does not itself establish or evaluate purpose; it can only judge the feasibility of desired objectives and provide their enabling mechanisms. Purpose must stem from man's collective wisdom and capacity for innovation. A "new" wisdom, imbued with scientific understanding but based on the totality of human experience, will have to come soon, for modern science and technology are rapidly pushing the power of man beyond the limits of the wisdom of the past. The strategy of the biomass has worked thus far, and man is the heir.

The crucial question is whether the strategy of man, which can now be consciously planned, will negate or promote the long cosmic progression of life.

Reference

DOBZHANSKY, T.
  Evolution, Genetics, and Man. New York, Wiley, 1963.

Index